SMITHSONIAN INSTITUTION
BUREAU OF AMERICAN ETHNOLOGY
BULLETIN 56

ETHNOZOOLOGY OF THE TEWA INDIANS

BY

JUNIUS HENDERSON

AND

JOHN PEABODY HARRINGTON

WASHINGTON
GOVERNMENT PRINTING OFFICE
1914

LETTER OF TRANSMITTAL

THE SCHOOL OF AMERICAN ARCHÆOLOGY,
Santa Fe, N. Mex., November 1, 1912.

DEAR SIR: I herewith transmit the manuscript of a paper entitled "Ethnozoology of the Tewa Indians," by Junius Henderson and John P. Harrington. I am authorized by the managing committee of The School of American Archæology to offer this work for publication by the Bureau of American Ethnology as a part of the results of the cooperative work of our respective institutions during 1910 and 1911.

I am, very truly, yours,

EDGAR L. HEWETT,
Director, The School of American Archæology.

Mr. F. W. HODGE,
Ethnologist in Charge,
Bureau of American Ethnology, Washington, D. C.

III

LETTER OF SUBMITTAL

SMITHSONIAN INSTITUTION,
BUREAU OF AMERICAN ETHNOLOGY,
Washington, D. C., November 22, 1912.

SIR: I have the honor to submit, with the recommendation that it be published as a bulletin of the Bureau of American Ethnology the manuscript of a memoir bearing the title "Ethnozoology of the Tewa Indians," by Junius Henderson and John P. Harrington.

This memoir embodies a part of the results of the joint researches conducted in New Mexico by the Bureau of American Ethnology and The School of American Archæology during 1910 and 1911.

Very respectfully,

F. W. HODGE,
Ethnologist in Charge.

Hon. CHARLES D. WALCOTT,
Secretary, Smithsonian Institution.

v

CONTENTS

PHONETIC KEY

It is necessary to preface this memoir with a key to the Tewa
sounds and the symbols adopted to represent them.

1. Orinasal vowels, pronounced with mouth and nose passages
open: ạ (Eng. father, but orinasal), ǣ (Eng. man, but orinasal),
ẹ (moderately close e, orinasal), ị (Portuguese sim), ǫ̈ (French pas,
but orinasal), ǫ (moderately close o, orinasal), ụ (Portuguese atum).

2. Oral vowels, pronounced with mouth passage open and nose
passage closed by the velum: a (Eng. father), e (moderately close e),
i (Eng. routine), o (moderately close o), u (Eng. rule).

An inverted period after a vowel symbol indicates that the vowel
is long. A superior vowel symbol indicates that the vowel is very
short and grating (knarrstimmig). The vowels are breathy, and
unless followed by the glottal stop, a glottalized stop, or a voiced
sound, an aspiration is distinctly heard toward the end.

3. Semi-vowels: j (Ger. ja, but very fricative), w (Eng. way).

4. Laryngeal consonants: h (laryngeal h), ' (glottal stop, lēnis).

5. Dorsal consonants: k (voiceless lēnis), kw (voiceless lēnis
labialized, Latin quis), k̓ (glottalized), k῾ (aspirated), g (Eng. finger,
voiced inflative g preplosively nasal), g̣ (Castilian abogado), qw
(Castilian juez), ŋ (Eng. singer), ŋw (Eng. Langworthy).

In absolute auslaut ŋ is somewhat palatal, also before ' and h.
Before frontal consonants ŋ is assimilated to n, before labial consonants to m.

6. Frontal consonants: ñ (Castilian mañana), t (voiceless lēnis),
t̟ (glottalized), t῾ (aspirated), ḍ (Eng. landing, inflative d preplosively
nasal), ᴊ (Japanese roku), ts (Ger. zehn, but very lēnis), t̂s (Ger. z,
glottalized), s (Eng. saw), tʃ (Eng. chew, but lēnis), t̂ʃ (Eng. chew,
glottalized), ʃ (Eng. ship) (ʃ is the capital of ʃ), n (Eng. now).

7. Labial consonants: p (voiceless lēnis), p̂ (glottalized), p̓,
(aspirated), ḅ (Eng. lambent, voiced inflative b preplosively nasal),
b̃ (Castilian caballo), m (Eng. man).

The sound of l is heard in some words of foreign origin, and in San
Ildefonso polamimi, 'butterfly'.

The consonants may also be classified as follows:

Voiced constringents: j, w.

Voiceless fricatives: h, s, ʃ.

Voiceless fricatives labialized: qw.

Voiceless lēnis sonoplosive clusives, labialized: *kw*.
Voiceless glottalized clusives: *ǩ, ǐ, p̂*.
Voiceless lēnis affricative clusives: *ts, tʃ*.
Voiceless glottalized affricative clusives: *t̂s, t̂ʃ*.
Voiceless aspirate clusives: *kʽ, tʽ, pʽ*.
Voiced inflative clusives, preplosively nasal: *g, ḍ, ḅ*.
Voiced lĕvis clusives: *g, ɹ, ƀ*.
Voiced nasals: *ŋ, ñ, n, m*.

The following phonems are consonant diphthongs: *qw, kw, ts, t̂s, tʃ, t̂ʃ, g, ḍ*, and *ḅ*. In the glottalized clusives (*ǩ, ǐ, t̂s, t̂ʃ, p̂*) the glottal plosion follows the oral plosion, even following the glided or sukūned *s* and *ʃ* of the consonantal diphthongs. That is, the *k, t, ts, tʃ*, or *p* is completely immersed in a glottal clusive. It has been determined that, at least in many instances, *g* and *g, ḍ* and *ɹ, ḅ* and *ƀ* are respectively but two aspects of the same phonem, as is the case with Castilian *g* and lĕvis *g, d* and lĕvis *d, b* and lĕvis *b*. The consonants occur in one length only. They may be more or less orinasal when contiguous to orinasal vowels. The sonancy of the voiceless lēnis clusives begins nearly simultaneously with the explosion.

A grave accent is placed over the vowel of a syllable weakly stressed. Strongly stressed syllables are unmarked. The intonation of the syllables is not indicated in this memoir.

PHONETIC SPELLING OF NON-TEWA WORDS

The symbols used in Tewa have the same value as in Tewa.

Sounds not occurring or not written in Tewa are indicated as follows: Vowels: *â* (French *patte*), *ă* (French *pas*), *ʉ* (unrounded *u*). The acute accent over a vowel indicates that it is loudly stressed. A circle under a vowel indicates that it is surd.

Consonants: ʽ (aspiration), [h] (a peculiar weak aspiration occurring in Jemez), κ (marginal or "velar" *k*, lēnis), *q* (Ger. a*ch*), *g, d, b* (as in Eng.); ꜰ (bilabial *f*) after a consonant symbol indicates palatalized or palatal quality.

ETHNOZOOLOGY OF THE TEWA INDIANS

By Junius Henderson and John Peabody Harrington [1]

GENERAL CONSIDERATIONS

THE fauna of a region, like its flora and geology, bears an intimate relation to the culture of its human inhabitants.[2] A nomadic people is generally of necessity dependent on animal life for sustenance, while a sedentary people, if numerous, remaining for a long period in permanent habitations, must be dependent more largely on direct products of the soil, except perhaps when living on the seashore, where almost inexhaustible fisheries furnish abundant food, or near the range of such animals as the caribou or the now nearly extinct American bison. A large number of people remaining constantly in one place and depending the year round on the game of the region would soon destroy their food supply. A nomadic tribe, wandering hither and thither, is constantly penetrating new game preserves and allowing the game in the old preserves to increase in abundance.

The ancient peoples, the remains of whose dwellings are found so abundantly in the country of the Tewa Indians, northwest of Santa Fe, New Mexico, were surely too numerous to have derived any considerable part of their sustenance for even a few months from the native mammals, birds, and other animals of the region, even if game were much more abundant than now, a condition which may well be doubted. If the simultaneous occupancy of only a small proportion of the ruins be supposed, there still would not have been enough game to support the population. However, it is probable that wild game formed an important supplement to the products of their cornfields and the native plants.

Bandelier [3] says of the region about the Rito de los Frijoles:

Game of all kinds, deer, elk, mountain sheep, bears, and turkeys, roamed about the region in numbers, and the brook afforded fish.

In a footnote he adds:

All the kinds of game mentioned were abundant around the Rito de los Frijoles in former times, but the communal hunts of the Pueblos, and later on the merciless slaughter of the Apaches, have greatly reduced it.

---

[1] The ethnological portion of this memoir is the work of Mr. Harrington, the zoological, that of Professor Henderson.

[2] Springer, Frank, The Field Session of the School of American Archæology, Science, n. s., XXXII, 623, 1910.

[3] Bandelier, A. F., Final Report of Investigations among the Indians of the Southwestern United States, Carried on Mainly in the Years from 1880 to 1885, Part II, Papers Archæol. Inst. Amer., Amer. ser., IV, 141, 1892.

Speaking of the region south of Santa Fe, Morrison [1] says:

Black, cinnamon, and occasionally grizzly bear, black and white-tailed deer, and turkeys, furnish abundant game to the Indian. The elk, once very plentiful in these mountains, is now very rarely seen.

Other statements of like nature may be found. It is certain that since the advent of the white man with his death-dealing rifle large game animals have greatly decreased in numbers nearly everywhere. Any reduction in the abundance of game in the area under discussion is probably due to promiscuous hunting at all seasons by both whites and Indians supplied with rifles, rather than to the communal hunts of the Pueblo Indians or to the raids of roving Apache. Careful consideration of all the facts bearing on the question leads to the conclusion that game never was very abundant about the Rito de los Frijoles. However this may be, it seems certain that it could not have remained abundant when the vicinity was occupied by the ancient inhabitants and still have furnished them with a large part of their food supply.

In his excellent paper on Pueblo environment, Hough [2] says:

It is difficult to realize the immense modification of animal and vegetable life which the white man has wrought in this region during the 30 years of his active occupancy. At the beginning of this period the region was well grassed and supplied with other vegetation adequate to the needs of vast herds of antelope, elk, and deer; rodent animals and birds were plentiful, and carnivores had abundance of prey. As a result of vegetation a humus had formed on all protected situations, rainfall was absorbed and equalized in distribution, and the terrific denudation which gashes the land at present was not begun.

The country was adapted to grazing and especially favorable on account of temperature and latitude, and at once great herds of cattle, horses and sheep were introduced from Texas where the range had failed. The result was that the range became overstocked, the grass disappeared under the tongues and hoofs of myriads of domestic animals, shrubs and trees were browsed and destroyed or swept away by fires, from certain regions species of plants vanished, and the land lay bare to the augmented winds and torrential rains. Trails became profound arroyos and the humus vanished in the streams and the surface of the country was stone, sand and gravel. Not the least of this baneful influence was the drying up of springs and other sources of water, and more than one observer collected data going to prove the progressive desiccation of the pueblo region. These facts must be borne in mind in discussion of the environment of the Southwest. As an example, it may be stated that in the exploration of one ancient pueblo at Winslow, Arizona, the bones of 37 species of animals were taken from the house refuse; it is not probable at present that a naturalist could collect 5 of these species from the environment. Wherever the explorer's spade has been put in the ancient ruins, facts of this character come to his notice, even if he has not heard the story from the early settlers or Indian traditionists.

While the baneful influence of overstocking the range and other follies of white settlers in parts of the West and the Southwest

---

[1] Executive and Descriptive Report of Lieutenant Charles C. Morrison, Sixth Cavalry, on the Operations of Party No. 2, Colorado Section, Field Season of 1877, in *Ann. Rep. U. S. Geog. Expl. and Surv. W. 100th Merid., for 1878*, p. 137, 1878.

[2] Hough, Walter, Pueblo Environment, *Proc. Amer. Asso. Adv. Sci.*, 55th meeting, 1906, pp. 450–51.

can not be ignored, the effects are but local. Vast areas in the Southwest have never been subjected to the ravages of large domestic herds, because from the time the region was first explored the lack of water has prohibited the use of many such areas for extensive grazing purposes. A study of the literature of early exploration does not indicate general distribution of vast herds of antelope, elk, and deer, and especially is this true of elk. Certainly within the period designated (30 years immediately preceding 1906) there has been no general distribution of large game in great herds, although antelope and deer have been abundant locally and are still common in places. It may be said of the species of animals whose bones have been taken from various pueblos that many of them may have been so rare that a naturalist might search the region for a year without seeing one. The bones represent the accumulated results of many hunting expeditions, more or less extensive, besides the daily hunting of many men for generations. An elk rib was taken from an ancient pueblo northwest of Santa Fe, yet old men from two neighboring pueblos say they have never seen an elk. Likewise the bison was known to many of the old Indians in the upper Rio Grande valley, although they had never seen one alive.

It is exceedingly probable that the important species inhabiting the Tewa region during the ancient occupancy were the same as at present, except the elk and mountain sheep, which have disappeared. The bison, no longer known in New Mexico in a wild state, was not found, perhaps, in this part of the Rio Grande valley and could be obtained only by barter or by long excursions through a country inhabited by hostile tribes. Though the present report lists a large number of animals for the region, a critical analysis shows that very few of them could have been important as a source of food.

In this connection the invertebrates may be almost wholly disregarded, though possibly in seasons of unusual abundance grasshoppers may have been a much-relished addition to the bill of fare; they were certainly much used farther west. It must be remembered, however, that invasions of these pests in sufficient numbers to make them important as a source of food for a large population would mean the destruction of the corn crops and of the grass and other vegetation on which the game animals feed, thus reducing the supply of the ordinary food of the human inhabitants. There were undoubtedly fish in all the important streams, but they could not have been numerous enough to have played a large part in sustaining the number of people who lived in the region, even if the latter were no more numerous than at the time of the Spanish conquest. Reptiles and amphibians may be wholly disregarded, as they do not occur in sufficient numbers to be important, though of course with a more abundant water supply there would have been more frogs. Most of the species of birds and mammals which occur abundantly are altogether too small and too difficult to obtain with crude weapons to be useful as food. Among the birds in this class may be mentioned nuthatches, hummingbirds, goldfinches, and sparrows. Robins and longcrested jays are also common, but a single meal for a fairsized clan would require all that are to be found in any one canyon. Piñon and Woodhouse's jays and mourning doves are abundant, probably as numerous now as they ever were, but not easy to secure even with modern weapons, and may be almost ignored as food birds for primitive people. Hawks, owls, and eagles are all too rare and too hard to obtain to be considered. During the autumn grouse and turkeys were probably obtainable in considerable numbers, and, with the ducks and other water birds along the river, constituted the only really important food birds of the region.

In case of the mammals, not infrequently a deer, elk, bear, or mountain sheep must have been obtained. With hundreds of people living on the mesas and in neighboring canyons, all constantly seeking to catch or kill these animals for food, we can not suppose their existence in much greater numbers than at present, when, though hunted with more effective weapons, they surely are not here hunted as persistently or by very many people. The same is true of the rabbits and squirrels. While they must have had constantly a small supply of such game, when the number of mouths awaiting it is considered, the meat diet of these ancient people was surely very limited. The other mammals were either too small or too rare to add materially to the food supply.

This region is almost undisturbed by civilization and therefore affords an excellent field for the naturalist as well as for the study of ethnozoology. There seems no good reason for supposing any great change in the fauna of the locality since the period of its occupancy by the people who constructed the pueblos and other dwellings long ago abandoned. Changes in faunas usually progress slowly, notwithstanding such conspicuous examples of rapid extermination or of introduction of species as are afforded by the bison, the passenger pigeon, and the English sparrow in America. Such examples, due to the superior facilities for destruction or introduction developed by the white race, are abnormal. It is quite possible that a few species besides elk and mountain sheep have disappeared from the vicinity within the period of human occupancy and that some others have extended their range into this area, though there is no evidence of such changes. The topography is certainly virtually the same as it has been for a very long period. If there has been since the beginning of human occupancy a general desiccation of the country sufficient to reduce the possibilities in the line of agriculture, it would not necessarily have produced much, if any, change in the native uncultivated flora, and without considerable change in topography and flora there would be little change in the fauna.[1]

In event of such desiccation some local migrations of species suggest themselves as possible. During August the writers found no blackbirds or meadowlarks on the mesas or in the canyons examined and conditions are not favorable to their regular presence there, but with somewhat greater precipitation moist meadows may have provided a suitable habitat for the redwings and cultivated upland areas near water may have attracted the meadowlarks. Both are now found in favorable localities in the Rio Grande valley. In a paper hereinafter cited Mrs. Bailey says that in San Miguel county the meadowlark occurs only in depressions in the plains where there is water. The limited distribution of water restricts the habitat of ducks and shore birds, which once may have been more generally distributed.

To understand fully the culture of a region it is necessary to know something of the native animals, especially those which have been useful to the people or which would have been noticed by them. The flesh of animals furnishes food, the skins provide raiment, thongs, and other useful products, and bones furnish awls and other implements; but perhaps even more important, from the cultural point of view, is the fact that animals enter largely into the mythology and religion of primitive peoples. The finding, in the ruins, of bones other than human may fairly be assumed to indicate that the animals to which they belonged were used by the former inhabitants for utilitarian, ornamental, or ceremonial purposes. In most cases the character of the animals, the condition of the bones, or the circumstances under which found suggests a marked probability as to the particular use. The culture, religion, and language of living peoples who are believed to be either directly descended from or closely related to the ancient inhabitants surely must throw much light on the subject. A large quantity of bones has been taken from the ruins of the Pajarito plateau, but the work of identification has not yet been completed.

It is not likely that in the use of animals for food the ancient inhabitants of this region differed much from those of northeastern Arizona. Discussing the bones found in the latter region, Hough[2] says:

The remains show that most of the animals of the region were consumed as food; but, as might be anticipated, bones of the carnivora are much rarer than those of the herbivora, the latter represented by deer and rabbit species, and the former by the fox, coyote, wolf, dog, raccoon, badger, wildcat, and puma, but no bones of the bear

---

[1] See Bulletins 54 and 55 of the Bureau of American Ethnology.

[2] Hough, Walter, Archeological Field Work in Northeastern Arizona (The Museum-Gates Expedition of 1901), *Ann. Rep. U. S. Nat. Mus. for 1901*, pp. 356–57, 1903.

were observed. Remains of the beaver and small rodents, and bones of birds, especially the turkey, eagle, hawk, and owl, were noted.

Remains of the dog and turkey were found in nearly every ruin, showing the extent of the domestication of these animals in this region. So far as can be determined, the dog and turkey were the only animals domesticated by the pueblo tribes. It was hoped that light might have been thrown upon the question of domestication of other animals, namely, the deer [citing Nadaillac] and an auchenia (llama), as affirmed by Cushing from figurines found on the Rio Salado, in Southern Arizona. The writer has copied numerous pictographs in the valley of the Little Colorado River showing unmistakably the herding of turkeys and of deer by men. . . . Still, the evidence presented so far as to the domestication of other animals than the dog and turkey is unsatisfactory.

Zoological field work was conducted for slightly less than four weeks in the neighborhood of El Rito de los Frijoles in August, 1910, so that this account can not be considered in any sense a final discussion of the fauna of the vicinity. Collection and observation were conducted chiefly in the lower part of the Rito de los Frijoles canyon and on adjacent mesas, but included a two-day trip to the Painted Cave and a three-day trip to the top of the Jemez Mountains and edge of Valle Grande, just beyond the headwaters of the Rito, so that a general impression of the fauna from the top of the mountains to the rim of the Rio Grande canyon was obtained. Judge A. J. Abbott, who now lives at El Rito de los Frijoles, Mr. Nathan Dowell, who has hunted and trapped in the region, and several of the Indians employed in the archeological excavations have furnished much information, which a short summer trip could not disclose. In case of the birds especially only observations carried through the four seasons could make it possible to secure a list even approximately complete, on account of the number of migratory species which must visit the vicinity. Obviously the birds seen were all either permanent or summer residents, winter residents and spring and autumn migrants being then absent. To the list have been added such species as have been recorded for the Rio Grande valley between the Colorado line and a point southwestward from Santa Fe, so far as they could be noted in the limited examination of the literature which has been possible. Time has not permitted as full an examination of the zoologic literature of the region as is desirable, and much information is hidden in works whose titles do not suggest at all the inclusion of anything zoologic.

The region is within the southern extremity of the great Rocky Mountain system. Northward, mountains extend in unbroken chains through Colorado. Southward, instead of continuous chains there are isolated mountain masses separated by dry mesas and plains. Consequently the affinities of the fauna as a whole are with the mountain fauna of Colorado. The great majority of species are found northward to or through Colorado. A few, as *Ashmunella*, are of distinctly southern type.

It was hoped to do a large amount of ethnozoologic work while in the field. Unforeseen circumstances prevented this except for a few hours of the last two days of the field season. Mr. Harrington, however, was able to do some independent work along that line in connection with his regular studies of the language of the Tewa. The Indian names given are in the San Juan dialect of the Tewa language, except where otherwise stated. The greater part of the discussion of methods in ethnobotany in Bulletin 55 applies with equal force to ethnozoology and needs not be repeated here.

Most of the animal names were obtained by exhibiting specimens to several Indians, including some of the older men of the tribe. Where specimens in hand were not available, care was taken to make sure of the identity of the animals named; this was easy, of course, in case of such readily described animals as the porcupine. In a few cases it was considered safe to use good colored plates figuring easily identified species; but wherever possible specimens in hand were exhibited and also the same species alive in their natural habitat. Where there is a question as to identity the name is either omitted or the doubt is expressed. It is always best to show informants also specimens of all species in the region which closely resemble one another and discover whether they really definitely distinguish them, and, if so, how. Care should always be taken not to suggest to them the answer to inquiries.

It is frequently said by unthinking or uninformed persons, who know something of the Indians' intimate knowledge of some phases of nature, that the American Indians know and have names for every species of plant and animal living in their vicinity. Inasmuch as some microscopic forms exist everywhere and as many macroscopic forms of invertebrates, as some insects, crustaceans, and mollusks, can be distinguished only by microscopic characters, the incorrectness of that idea is evident. The Indians are usually correct in distinguishing the larger and better-marked species of birds and mammals, but they certainly do not recognize some of the minute differences which are of more importance than some of those more easily observed. They distinguish species more closely than the average white man who has not had zoologic training. Though several species of jackrabbits and several cottontails inhabit the region over which these Indians have roamed, they seem to recognize but one species of each. However, the majority of white men could not do more. The Pueblo Indians who claim the Jemez Plateau as the home of their ancestors are agriculturists, not hunters, though they do some hunting, of course, just as white farmers do. It would be interesting and important to make a thorough comparative study of the knowledge of natural history possessed by agricultural tribes and hunting tribes.

To insure accuracy, such a study, as is true, indeed, of all ethno-zoological and ethnobotanical work, should be cooperative, trained zoologists, botanists, and ethnologists working together in the field.

Indians differ as much individually as do other races in their capacity, experience, and opportunity for observation and in their interest in the mysteries of Nature. One person may have had abundant opportunity for the observation of the various species of deer, but paying slight attention to the little chipmunks and hence not distinguishing the different kinds of the latter, while with another person the reverse may be the case. Hence the information obtained from a single informant may not at all represent the knowledge or ideas of his people. This makes it advisable whenever possible to check the information obtained by enlisting the services of several informants.

It is too early for sweeping generalizations, but a few general remarks seem safe. Indian nomenclature as a whole recognizes differences, not relationships. There is little, if any, evidence of the classification by the Indian of species in consanguineous groups, as orders, families, and genera, except in very obvious cases. Whether he does so arrange them in his mind, even though he does not express the idea in his nomenclature, is very doubtful and should be more fully investigated. In such investigations there is always danger of recording opinions which have been more or less influenced by contact with whites, a contingency which should be guarded against. In most cases a species is perhaps considered a distinct entity, not connected with any other species. However, their recognition of several kinds of bear, deer, etc., may indicate some sort of an idea of genetic relationship which further study may elucidate. A thorough knowledge of the language is necessary to a real understanding of this subject. The writers found them using the English word "rat" for several species of squirrels and chipmunks, yet in their own language they have usually distinct names for each. Such cases as the bear, to which the Mohave in their own language apply a name meaning "great badger", should be followed up to ascertain whether it indicates a supposed relationship. It may well be doubted whether the use by the Hopi of the same name for such distinct species as the Harris ground-squirrel and Say's ground-squirrel, and with slightly different pronunciation for two small chipmunks, indicates a failure to distinguish them. Our San Ildefonso informants, while applying the same name to such different species as Say's ground-squirrel and the little chipmunk, showed clearly by their comments that they did not consider them the same species. The solution of the problem requires a determination of the Indian's conception of species, if he has any, which is not a simple task. Europeans and their American descendants have been familiar for generations with modern scientific ideas of species, their interrelations, and the development of various groups of species from common sources. In discussing such matters, one's words, whether one speaks in his own language or attempts to apply a primitive language, represent definite mental concepts, but may convey to primitive people, who have not such concepts, ideas quite foreign to those intended. So also we are in constant danger of unconsciously injecting our own concepts into the words used by our informants in expressing their ideas. It is exceedingly difficult to question them about abstract ideas without framing the queries so as to suggest one's own views and thus color the replies.

Care must be taken to avoid mistaking descriptive or comparative terms for names. When an Indian informant is shown a foreign species with which he is not familiar, he may, as is the case with a representative of any other race, designate it by what appears to be a name but which on analysis proves to be a descriptive or comparative word or phrase and not a native name for the species, as when a small white marine shell is exhibited and a word is applied which means that it looks like bone.

That the Indians have been close observers of animals is shown by the fact that they have developed names for almost all the parts of birds and mammals, as claws, whiskers, foot-pads, etc.

If work in ethnozoology is to be maintained on a scientific basis and an accurate estimate made of the Indian's knowledge of Nature, definite determinations of the species of plants and animals discussed must be made. Much of the work hitherto done in obtaining the names of plants and animals has been worthless, because no attempt was made to discover and record with certainty the kind of plants and animals to which the names are applied. Much more important than mere nomenclature is the idea of which nomenclature is but an attempted expression. The best way certainly is to get the information in the field, so far as possible by showing the Indian informants the animal in its natural environment. Specimens thus identified and discussed should then be scientifically identified and preserved for future reference.

CLASSIFICATION OF ANIMALS

There is no word meaning 'animal'. *'Animąŋ* or *'animal* (<Span. *animal*) is sometimes heard.

No word meaning 'mammal' is in use. Bats are considered birds. *Ṭowà*, 'human being', distinguishes man from other animals, and sometimes Tewa or again all Indians from other kinds of men.

Hǽ·pąŋ now applies to large domestic animals, as horses, cattle, swine. What it referred to in pre-European times is uncertain.

Pokanu signifies game or game animals, including not only game beasts, as deer, buffalo, rabbits, bears, mountain sheep, etc., but also game birds and other animals whose flesh is relished as an important food. In a Taos myth[1] the game animals (Tewa *pokanu*) are said to inhabit a great estufa situated somewhere in the west from which they are at times driven forth for the benefit of the Indians. No such information has been obtained from the Tewa.

Tsiʌe is the almost exact equivalent of English 'bird', referring to all species of birds and bats. In one compound, *po·tsiʌe*, 'water bird' (*po·*, water; *tsiʌe*, bird) it refers to an insect. Gatschet gives Tewa "*tohi-e*", 'bird'.[2] Compare Taos *tsijuunâ;* Piro (Bartlett's vocabulary) "*tsi-ki-é*"; Jemez *sejiw;* Southern Ute, *witʃitsi̧;* Hopi (Gatschet), "*tohi-i*".[3]

There is no general name for reptiles or lizards.

Pæñu, 'snake', parallels in usage English 'snake'. Cf. Taos *pætsuenâ;* Piro (Bartlett's vocabulary) "*pe-tsun-to-yar-é*"; Jemez *hajă;* Keres (Gatschet), "*shu-ui*"[4]; Hopi (Gatschet) "*tohu-ash*".[5]

'O·ku· appears to apply to any kind of turtle or tortoise.

Po·qwæ· applies to salamanders.

P'ę·ŋkwą̊ŋ applies to frogs and toads.

Pa· means 'fish.' Cf. Taos *pöünâ;* Isleta *puiʌe;* Piro (Bartlett's vocabulary) "*pu-é*"; Jemez *po;* Hopi *pakʲo'ö.*

There is no word meaning 'insect.'

Puɓæ, 'worm,' may be loosely applied to all worm-like animals, perhaps even to insects and spiders; but this latter application is not usually made.

'Ą́'wæ· refers to any kind of spider.

There is no word referring to crustaceans in general.

There is no general name for mollusks or even molluscan shells. *'Oɓe* comes the nearest to being such a name. See under Mollusks below.

Ku·pi·, literally 'red stone' (*ku·*, stone; *pi·*, red), refers to red coral. Perhaps any coral might be indicated by adding *wa·gì*, 'like', to this name.

All names of animals have the same form in singular and plural number unless an adjective with gender-number postfix be a part of the name or the name be compounded with certain words denoting age and sex.

The age-sex nouns are postjoined to the animal names. With the exception of some animal names derived from the Spanish, the Tewa

[1] *American Anthropologist*, n. s., XII, pp. 40–41, 1910.
[2] A. S. Gatschet, Zwölf Sprachen aus dem Südwesten Nordamerikas, Weimar, 1876, p. 39.
[3] Ibid.
[4] Ibid.
[5] Ibid.

animal name does not show sex or age of the animal to which it refers
unless one of these age-sex nouns is postjoined.

As applied to *įowà*, 'human beings,' the following age-sex nouns
are used, and used alone, the word *įowà* being regularly omitted and
understood.

'*E·*, 'child,' 'son,' 'daughter'; 2+ plural '*e·ñæ·*.

'*A'ᵃñu·ke·*, 'young girl'; 2+ plural '*a'ᵃñu·ŋ'e·ñæ·*.

'*E'ᵉnu·ke·*, 'young boy'; 2+ plural '*e'ᵉnu·ŋ'e·ñæ·*.

'*A'ᵃñu·*, 'girl at adolescence'; 2+ plural '*a'ᵃñu·ŋ*.

'*E'ᵉnu·*, 'boy at adolescence'; 2+ plural '*e'ᵉnu·ŋ*.

Kwi·, 'woman in prime'; 2+ plural *kwi·ñæ'ᵆŋ*.

Sę·ŋ, 'man in prime'; 2+ plural *sę·ŋñæ'ᵆŋ*.

Kwi·jo·, 'old woman'; 2+ plural *kwi·jo·*. The singular has falling
intonation in the second syllable, the 2+ plural has circumflex intonation in the second syllable.

Sę·ŋḑo·, 'old man'; 2+ plural *sę·ŋḑa·*.

When these age-sex nouns are applied to lower animals the plural
of '*e* is '*e·*, the singular having falling, the 2+ plural circumflex, intonation, and '*e'ᵉnu·ke·* and '*a'ᵃñu·ke·* and their plurals are not used.

In the case of animal-denoting names which have been borrowed
from the Spanish, sex and age are denoted both by the Tewa method
of postjoining sex-age nouns and by the Spanish method of employing
different endings or different words. One hears, for instance, both
kaḅajùkwi·, 'horse female' (*kaḅajù*, horse; *kwi·*, female), and *jewà*
(<Spanish *yegua*) meaning 'mare'.

Barring words of Spanish origin, only one instance is known of a
special word being employed to signify the young of a species of
animal. This is *mǫ̀ǵè*, 'young of the mule deer,' which can also be
called *pæ·'e·*, 'little mule deer' (*pæ·*, mule deer; '*e·*, diminutive).[1]

Perhaps the majority of Tewa animal names are unetymologizable.
There are not many instances where more than one name is applied
to an animal species. The additional name is regularly descriptive.
Thus owls may be called *mǫhuŋ*, or *tsiso'jo·*, 'big eyes '(*tsi*, eye;
so'jo·, big). The Franciscan Fathers have recorded many additional
names of this kind from the Navaho.

We find no unetymologizable additional names of animals like our
European Kosenamen or Sagenamen, unless it be *poseqwasę·ŋḑo·*, an
additional name of *ḑe·*, coyote. Thus we call the bear '*bear*' or '*Bruin*',
the German calls the bear '*bär*' or '*Petz*', the Russian calls the bear
'*mⁱedvⁱédʲ*' or *Mⁱ́ʃka*, and *Bruin, Petz, Mⁱ́ʃka* have no etymology
known to the people. But the Tewa call the bear *ke·* and only *ke·*,
or if there is an additional name it is descriptive and its etymology
is understood by all. *Poseqwasę·ŋḑo·*, applied to the coyote, is the
only exception discovered thus far.

[1] Cf. the two Tewa names for 'milkweed' at different stages of its growth, in *Bulletin 55, Bur. Amer. Ethn.*

A number of names of introduced animals which have been borrowed from the Spanish are supplanted by additional names for these animals, of Tewa derivation, when speaking in the presence of Mexicans, lest they understand. The same is also the practice in the case of 'watermelon' and some other plant names.

ANNOTATED LIST OF ANIMALS

MAMMALS

Ṭowà.

Homo sapiens.

Ṭowà means human being, person, folks, people, clan. Unlike the Tewa names of other animals *ṭowà* is never coupled with sex-age nouns, being regularly omitted when these are applied to human beings. Thus *tsekwi·*, 'female dog in prime' (*tse*, dog; *kwi·*, female in prime), but merely *kwi·*, 'human woman in prime.' Human beings are not considered by the Tewa to be essentially different from other animals.

The races of man are called *ṭowà.*

The word *ṭowà* often refers especially to Indian people as distinguished from other people. Americans are called *Meẕikanù ṭowà*, 'American people' (*Meẕikanù*, American, <Span. *Americano; ṭowà*, person, people). Mexicans are called *Kwæ̣ku·ŋṭowà* (*Kwæ̣ku·ŋ*, of uncertain etymology; *ṭowà*, person, people). Negroes are called *Kwæ̣ku·ŋṭowà p'e·ŋniŋ*, 'black Mexicans' (*Kwæ̣ku·ŋṭowà*, Mexican, *p'e·ŋ*, black). The Chinese are called *Tsinùṭowà*, Chinaman people (*Tsinù*, Chinaman <Span. *Chino; ṭowà*, person, people).

Monù (<Span. *mono*).

Monkey.

The Tewa know that monkeys live in Mexico. They say that monkeys look like men: *ṭowàwa·gì*, 'like a human being' (*ṭowà*, human being; *wa·gì*, like). An organ-grinder with a monkey visited San Ildefonso last year.

Sip'i.

Corynorhinus macrotis pallescens Miller. Pale Big-eared Bat.

Corynorhinus macrotis Le Conte was reported at Santa Fe by Allen[1] in 1893. As *macrotis* is a Southeastern form, the Santa Fe specimen is much more likely referable to the subspecies *pallescens*, described in 1897 by Miller,[2] which ranges from Colorado and Utah southward into Mexico.

Sip'i.

Myotis lucifugus longicrus (True). Little Brown Bat.

---

[1] Allen, Harrison, A Monograph of the Bats of North America, *Bull. U. S. Nat. Museum*, no. 43, p. 57, 1893.

[2] Miller, Gerrit S., Revision of the North American Bats of the Family Vespertilionidæ, *North American Fauna*, no. 13, Biol. Surv., U. S. Dept. Agr., pp. 52–53, 1897.

Reported at Santa Fe by Miller.[1]

We observed bats at El Rito de los Frijoles in the evenings of the first ten days in August, 1910, but saw none later, and failed to obtain any for identification.

Bats are classed with birds by the Tewa, although the Mexicans of the Tewa country call them *ratones voladores*, 'flying rats or mice.' *Sip'i* is said to be applied to any species of bat.

Ko'ǫη (akin to Taos *kanená*, buffalo).

Bison bison (Linn.). American Bison, Buffalo.

Although the bison, its habits, and methods of hunting it, are known to the Tewa by hearsay, it appears that very few individuals have ever seen a bison alive. Old Diego Roybal of San Ildefonso, although he loves to tell about the bison, has never seen one. J. M. Naranjo of Santa Clara has seen bison on the plains "about halfway between here and Saint Louis." In former times the Tewa trafficked in the skins and other products, and occasionally hunted the animal on the plains to the eastward, before its extermination there. Whole bison skins or portions of them, with the hair on, are still to be found among the Tewa and are used as "medicine" (*wo*) and for other purposes. Bison horns are also used as headdresses in the bison dance (*ko'ǫη farè*) held at San Ildefonso on January 24th of each year.

The Tewa do not know that the bison ever ranged in or west of their country. Dr. Allen, in his monograph on the bison,[2] says:

I have found no record of their existence in the highlands of New Mexico, or anywhere to the westward or southward of Santa Fe.

Bandelier,[3] commenting on a Spanish place-name of the region south of Santa Fe, says:

One of these bears the name "Ojo del Cibolo." This seems to imply that the buffalo once ranged as far as the base of the San Francisco and San Pedro Mountains.

Hornaday, on his map showing the extermination of the bison,[4] gives 1840 as the date of its extermination in the Rio Grande Valley of northern New Mexico and places the limit of its former range in western New Mexico.

In another place in his monograph (p. 474) Dr. Allen qualifies his statement hereinbefore quoted, under the subheading, "Probable extent of its former range," as follows:

Westward it extended over northern New Mexico and then westward and northward throughout the great Salt Lake Basin.

---

[1] Miller, Gerrit S., op. cit., pp. 64–65.

[2] Allen, J. A., History of the American Bison, Bison americanus, *Ninth Ann. Rep. U. S. Geol. & Geog. Surv. Terr. for 1875* (Hayden Survey), p. 517, 1877.

[3] Bandelier, A. F., Final Report of Investigations among the Indians of the Southwestern United States, Carried on Mainly in the Years from 1880 to 1885, Part II, *Papers of the Archæological Institute of America, American Series*, IV, p. 254, 1892.

[4] Hornaday, William T., The Extermination of the American Bison, *Ann. Rep. U. S. Nat. Museum for 1887*, 1889.

In a note dated February 27, 1911, in reference to this latter statement, he says:

I am able to qualify the last part of that statement on the basis of hitherto unpublished information received from Dr. Edward Palmer, the well-known natural history collector, who wrote me that in 1870 he found bison bones, some of them in a good state of preservation, about 20 miles west of Fort Wingate, N. Mex., and hence not far from the boundary line between Arizona and New Mexico. This will bring its former range to the latitude of Santa Fe. My present belief is that it formerly ranged over northwestern New Mexico.

Bison bones were found deep in the débris of a cave on the upper Tularosa River, in western Socorro County, N. Mex., by Dr. Walter Hough, but these may have been brought from a distance and deposited in the cave for ceremonial purposes.[1]

Hodge gives as Bison clans at various pueblos: San Ildefonso, *Kóo-tdóa;* Pecos, *Tâshtyë'+;* Acoma, *Moshaích-hanoq^{ch};* Sia, *Mushä'ch-háno.*

> *Kuwà* (akin to Isleta *koarè,* Ovis canadensis), or *p̂i·ŋkuwà* (*p̂i·ŋ,* mountain; *kuwà,* Ovis canadensis). *P̂i·ŋ,* 'mountain', is prejoined to distinguish this animal from the domestic sheep and goat, to which the name *kuwà* is also applied; see below.

Ovis canadensis Shaw. Mountain Sheep, Bighorn.

This species was reported near Santa Fe in 1873 by Coues and Yarrow.[2] Bandelier[3] says:

In 1880 I saw the last mountain sheep at the Rito. That beautiful animal has now completely disappeared from the Valles range.

Heads have been found in the ruins of the plateau.

The animal is well known to the Tewa, though very few of them have ever seen it alive. Diego Roybal and other old hunters are fond of telling the widespread but absurd story of how this animal when pursued throws itself over a cliff and alights uninjured on its horns.

> *Kuwà* (akin to Isleta *koarè* (see above), meaning originally Ovis canadensis, mountain sheep).

Domestic Sheep.

The male sheep is usually called *kuwàsę·ŋ,* 'male sheep' (*kuwà,* sheep; *sę·ŋ,* male), but *ǵaneлù*(<Span. *carnero*) is also heard. Lambs are regularly called *kuwà'e·,* 'little sheep' (*kuwà,* sheep; *'e·,* diminutive). When it is desired to distinguish a sheep from a goat one may

[1] Lyon, M. W., jr., Mammal Remains from Two Prehistoric Village Sites in New Mexico and Arizona, *Proc. U. S. Nat. Museum,* XXXI, pp. 647–49, 1906.

[2] Coues, Elliott, and Yarrow, H. C., Report upon the Collections of Mammals Made in Portions of Nevada, Utah, California, Colorado, New Mexico, and Arizona During the Years 1871, 1872, 1873, and 1874, *U. S. Geog. Explor. & Surv. W. of 100th Merid.* (Wheeler Survey), V, pp. 68–69, 1875.

[3] Bandelier, A. F., Final Report of Investigations Among the Indians of the Southwestern United States, Carried on Mainly in the years from 1880 to 1885, Part II, *Papers Archæol. Inst. Amer., Amer. Ser.,* IV, p. 141, 1892.

say *kuwà p'opa·'i'ⁱ*, 'cracked haired sheep' (*kuwà*, sheep; *p'o*, hair; *p̂a·*, cracked).

Very few of the Tewa own sheep, and the flocks consist of a few animals only. The sheep are never milked.

> *Kuwà* (akin to Isleta *koarè* (see above), meaning originally vis canadensis, mountain sheep).

Domestic Goat.

If it is desired to distinguish goat from sheep, one may say *kuwà p'o'ą́ñǽ·'i'ⁱ*, 'smooth haired goat' (*kuwà*, sheep, goat; *p'o*, hair; *'ą́ñǽ·*, smooth, not cracked or rough like a sheep's hair). The male goat is called *kuwàsę·ŋ*, 'male goat' (*kuwà*, goat; *sę·ŋ*, male) or *tsiⁱbatù* (<Span. *chibato*).

Few goats are kept by the Tewa. Goats are milked, usually by the women.

> *Tǫŋ.*
> *Antilocapra americana* (Ord.). Antelope, Pronghorn.

This species is still found alive in parts of New Mexico and was known to the cliff-dwellers of the Rito de los Frijoles. An old San Ildefonso Indian says that he formerly hunted antelope on the Pajarito Plateau, mostly near the Rio Grande Canyon, but they are now all gone.

Speaking of the dry valley between the Sierra de los Dolores and the Sierra de San Francisco, south of the Tewa country, Bandelier [1] says that "in most places it is grassy, and haunted by antelopes."

Hodge gives as Antelope clans of various Pueblos: San Ildefonso, *Toⁿ-tdóa;* Isleta, *T'am-t'aínïn;* Laguna, *Kǔr'tsi-hánoᶜʰ;* Acoma, *Kǔr'ts-hánoqᶜʰ;* Sia, *Kǔ'ts-háno;* San Felipe, *Kúuts-hano;* Cochiti, *Kǔ'ts-hánuch.* An antelope which destroyed human beings figures in Sia mythology.

> *Ta·* (akin to Taos *töünemâ*).
> *Cervus canadensis* Erxl. Wapiti, American Elk.

It appears that there are no elk now in the region, according to both Indian and white informants, though the species above mentioned formerly ranged southward into the mountains of northern New Mexico. Bandelier [2] rather indefinitely reports it at El Rito de los Frijoles. Two San Ildefonso Indians who have hunted much informed the writers that they were familiar with the species from having seen it in southern Colorado, but had never known it on the Pajarito Plateau. Cope [3] says:

---

[1] Bandelier, A. F., Final Report of Investigations among the Indians of the Southwestern United States, Carried on Mainly in the Years from 1880 to 1885, Part II, *Papers Archæol. Inst. Amer., Amer. Ser.,* IV, p. 106, 1892.

[2] Bandelier, A. F., op. cit., p. 141.

[3] Cope, E. D., Report on the Geology of that Part of Northwestern New Mexico Examined During the Field Season of 1874, *Ann. Rep. U. S. Geog. Explor. & Surv. W. of 100th Merid., for 1875,* p. 92; Report upon the Extinct Vertebrata Obtained in New Mexico by Parties of the Expedition of 1874, ibid., 1877, IV, pt. II, p. 18.

In exploring the hills of this formation along the Puerco, I found the horns of an elk (*Cervus canadensis*). This locality must be near the southern limit of its range. I learned that it is not uncommon on the high plateau near Tierra Amarilla on the northeast.

Morrison,[1] writing of the mountains more than a hundred miles south of Santa Fe, reported that "the elk, once very plentiful in these mountains, is now very rarely seen." The latter may refer to another species of elk, *Cervus merriami* Nelson, whose range is given as the White Mountains of Arizona and the Mongollon Mountains of New Mexico. One or the other species of this noble animal was doubtless known to the ancient inhabitants of El Rito de los Frijoles.

According to information obtained from an aged Indian of Santa Clara pueblo by Miss B. W. Freire-Marrecq, elk of the smaller sort, not so large as the great elk, are rarely seen in the mountains north of the Tewa country. What animal is really meant was not ascertained.

> *Pæ·* (akin to Taos *pænâ*, Isleta *pị'iɹè*, 2+ plu. *pịmnin*, Bartlett's Piro "pi-ye," Jemez *pâ*).

Odocoileus hemionus (Raf.). Mule Deer, Colorado Black Tail.

A young deer of this species is called by the Tewa either *pæ·'e.* (*pæ·*, mule deer; *'e·*, diminutive), or *mą̂gè*. The latter word can not be etymologized, and is the only animal name of Tewa origin known to the writers which is applied only to the young of a species.

The cured skin of *pæ·* and also of the western white-tailed deer and the elk is called *pujè*, this word being commonly applied to the cured skin of these three animals only. The fresh skin or the skin on the animal is known as *pæ·k·owà*, 'deer skin' (*pæ·*, Odocoileus hemionus; *k·owà*, tegument, skin).

Hodge gives as Deer clans of various pueblos: San Ildefonso, *Päⁿ-tdóa;* Santa Clara, *Pä-tdóa;* Isleta, *Pim-t'aínïn;* Pecos, *Pa'+;* Sia and San Felipe, *Dyáni-hano;* Zuñi, *Shóhoita-kwe*. The mule deer is prominent in Tewa mythology.

This is the common Deer of the region. We saw but one (a doe) while at Frijoles canyon, but three others were reported by the Indians while we were there. Even Tewa boys are aware that "a lady deer is without antlers." It is said that deer of this species were plentiful in former times, and deer products were much used by the Tewa.

> *Hụ̂a·pæ·* 'dry juniper deer' (*hụ*, 'one-seeded juniper', Juniperus monosperma; *îa·*, 'dryness', 'dry'; *pæ·*, 'mule deer', *Odocoileus hemionus* Raf.).

? ———

This is said to be a species of deer distinct from the *pæ·*.

---

[1] Morrison, Charles C., Executive and Descriptive Report of Lieut. Charles C. Morrison, Sixth Cavalry, on the Operations of Party No. 2, Colorado Section, Field Season of 1877. *Ann. Rep. U. S. Geog. Explor. & Surv. W. of 100th Merid.*, for 1878, p. 137, 1878.

'Ohuɲ.
Odocoileus americanus macrourus (Raf.).   Western White-tailed
    Deer.
This is the Tewa name of the animal known in New Mexican
Spanish as *cola larga*.   The *'ohuɲ* is mentioned in Tewa myths as one
of the larger game animals.   The cured skin of the *'ohuɲ*, as well as
that of the mule deer and the elk, is called *pujè*, 'deerskin', 'buckskin'.
We have questioned only three San Ildefonso Indians concerning
this species of deer.   They stated that the *pæ·* and *'ohuɲ* differ only
as regards the tail, the form of the antlers and the body-color being
the same.   It is evident that they had not closely observed the
antlers and the general color.

Pu·.
Lepus campestris Bach.   White-tailed Jackrabbit.
Jackrabbits are reported by both whites and Indians, but with
no information as to the species.   The white-tailed form is reported
by Nelson.[1]

Pu·.
Lepus bairdi Hayden.   Rocky Mountain Snowshoe Rabbit.
Recorded from 30 miles north of Taos and from Chama by Nelson,[2]
and from Taos by Coues and Yarrow.[3]

Pu·.
Lepus callotis Wagler ?   White-sided Jackrabbit.
Reported at San Pedro, N. Mex., about 35 or 40 miles south of
El Rito de los Frijoles, in 1873, by Coues and Yarrow.[4]   As this is
far beyond the supposed range of the species, perhaps it should be
referred to the next.

Pu·.
Lepus californicus texianus Waterhouse.   Texas Jackrabbit.
We have no record of this species from the Pajarito Plateau, but
New Mexico, except the northeastern part, is included within its
range,[5] so it should be looked for in our area.

Pu·.
Domestic rabbit, domestic hare.
The name was originally applied to jackrabbits.

Pu·.
Pu·wa·gì, 'jackrabbit like' (*pu·*, jackrabbit; *wa·gì*, like).
Guinea pig.

1 Nelson, E. W., The Rabbits of North America, *North American Fauna*, No. 29, Biol. Surv., U. S.
Dept. Agr., pp. 74, 78, 1909.
2 Nelson, E. W., op. cit., pp. 109–12.
3 Coues, Elliott, and Yarrow, H. C., op. cit., p. 126.
4 Ibid.
5 Nelson, E. W., op. cit., pp. 142–45

Pu· means jackrabbit, domestic rabbit, domestic hare; with or without *wa·gì*, 'like', it is applied to guinea pigs.

Kwą́ŋ.

Sylvilagus nuttalli pinetis (Allen).   Rocky Mountain Cottontail.

Recorded by Nelson [1] from many northern New Mexico localities, including Costillo Pass, Gallinas Mountains, Jemez Mountains, Hall's Peak (southeast of Taos), San Antonio Mountains, Santa Clara Mountains, Taos Mountain, Tierra Amarilla, Tres Piedras, and Twining (near Taos).   We saw several, which were probably this species or the next, at and near El Rito de los Frijoles, but did not obtain specimens for identification.

Kwą́ŋ.

Sylvilagus auduboni warreni Nelson.   Colorado Cottontail.

Recorded by Nelson [2] from San Antonio Mountains, Tres Piedras, and other localities in northwestern New Mexico.

The New Mexico cottontail (*Sylvilagus auduboni neomexicanus* Nelson) appears to range from the Pecos Valley eastward, hence it does not come within our area.

Sǫ·ŋ.

Erethizon epixanthum Brandt.   Yellow-haired Porcupine.

We saw no signs of porcupines about El Rito de los Frijoles.   At the old Buckman sawmill, at the base of the mountains, we saw the skin of one which had been killed there.   San Ildefonso Indians report its occurrence in the mountains and sometimes in the fields, and are familiar with its habit of gnawing the bark of trees.   The smaller hairs are called *p'o* and the large spine-like hairs *ŋwæ·*, a word which is applied also to the thorns of plants.   The Indians believe that when angry the *sǫ·ŋ* has the power of shooting these *ŋwæ·* like arrows.

Pe·, or *pe·ʌa* (*pe·*, Zapus princeps; *ʌa*, unexplained).

? *Zapus princeps* Allen.   Rocky Mountain Jumping Mouse.

Reported at Camp Burgwyn [3] [Cantonment Burgwin] and Santa Fe by Preble.[4]   Both whites and Indians describe a mouselike animal with long, kangaroo-like hind legs and short forelegs, at El Rito de los Frijoles, but we did not succeed in catching any for identification, and can not feel sure from the description that it is a jumping mouse.   One Indian reported that *pe·* is smaller than the deermouse, and *pe·ʌa* considerably larger.   They may represent some species of pocket mouse and a kangaroo rat.

---

[1] Nelson, E. W., op. cit., pp. 207–11.

[2] Ibid., pp. 231–32.

[3] The Cantonment Burgwin specimen has been referred to a distinct species, *Zapus luteus*. See Miller in *Proc. Biol. Soc. Washington*, XXIV, p. 253, Dec. 23, 1911. Miller also reports *Z. luteus* from Española, Taos County, and from Cloudcroft, Otero County.

[4] Preble, Edward A., Revision of the Jumping Mice of the Genus Zapus, *North American Fauna*, no. 15, Biol. Surv., U. S. Dept. Agr., pp. 22–23, 1899.

Ŋwįʼ·ŋ.
Perognathus flavescens Merriam.   Plains Pocket Mouse.
Reported at Santa Fe by Osgood.[1]

Ŋwįʼ·ŋ.
Perognathus flavus Baird.   Baird's Pocket Mouse.
Reported at Taos by Osgood.[2]

Ŋwįʼ·ŋ.
Perognathus apache Merriam.   Apache Pocket Mouse.
Reported at Española, San Pedro, and Santa Fe, by Osgood.[3]

Tʃugì.
Thomomys aureus pervagus Merriam.   Roaming Pocket Gopher.
The type locality is Española.[4]
Gopher mounds are abundant at El Rito de los Frijoles, but we obtained no specimens of the gopher for identification. They may be this species, which was described from a locality not far away. The Indians accurately described the habits of the animal in digging its holes, pushing the earth out to form a mound, and then covering the entrance with earth by working from within.

? ———
Microtus mordax Merriam.   Cantankerous Vole, Field Mouse.
Reported at Chama by Bailey.[5]
A good line of traps repeatedly set in all sorts of places at El Rito de los Frijoles failed to catch any voles or indeed any of the mammals smaller than chipmunks except deer-mice.

? ———
Fiber zibethicus osoyoosensis Lord.   Muskrat.
Reported at Rinconada (north of Santa Fe), by Hollister,[6] who also records *F. z. pallidus* Mearns at Albuquerque.

Pini'i?
Neotoma albigula Hartley.   White-throated Wood Rat.
Reported at Abiquiu, Chama Canyon, Española, San Pedro, Santa Clara Canyon, Rinconado, etc., by Goldman.[7]
Both whites and Indians described a bluish-gray, round-tailed rat which gathers piñon nuts for winter food at El Rito de los Frijoles, and we saw one nest which seemed to be that of a wood rat. No specimens were obtained for identification. San Ildefonso Indians

---

[1] Osgood, Wilfred H., Revision of the Pocket Mice of the Genus Perognathus, *North American Fauna*, no. 18, Biol. Surv., U. S. Dept. Agr., pp. 20–21, 1900.

[2] Ibid., pp. 23–24.

[3] Ibid., pp. 26–27.

[4] Merriam, C. Hart, Descriptions of Twenty-Three New Pocket Gophers of the Genus Thomomys, *Proc. Biol. Soc. Wash.*, XIV, p. 110, 1901.

[5] Bailey, Vernon, Revision of American Voles of the Genus Microtus, *North American Fauna*, no. 17, Biol. Surv., U. S. Dept. Agr., pp. 49–50, 1900.

[6] Hollister, N., A Systematic Synopsis of the Muskrats, *North American Fauna*, no. 32, Biol. Surv., U. S. Dept. Agr., p. 26, 1911.

[7] Goldman, Edward A., Revision of the Wood Rats of the Genus Neotoma, *North American Fauna*, no. 31, Biol. Surv., U. S. Dept. Agr., pp. 31–33, 1910.

also told of *pini'i*, a big whitish rat, with a very bad odor which they compare to that of a skunk, at Ojo Caliente.

Qwǽ·ŋ?

Neotoma mexicana fallax Merriam. Colorado or Gale's Wood Rat.

Reported from Chama River, Gallina, Gallinas Mountains, Tres Piedras, Twining, etc., by Goldman.[1]

Qwǽ·ŋjo· (*qwǽ·ŋ*, Neotoma mexicana fallax Merriam?; *jo·*, augmentative).

Neotoma cinerea orolestes Merriam. Colorado Bushy-tailed Wood Rat.

Reported from Agua Fria, Chama, Costillo Pass, Jemez Mountains, Taos, Taos Mountains, Tierra Amarilla, Tres Piedras, Twining, etc., by Goldman.[2]

This is the animal known through the southern Rocky Mountains as the "mountain rat" and "pack rat," but is called by Goldman, in his Revision, the "Colorado bushy-tailed wood rat."

Ŋwi̥·ŋ.

Peromyscus maniculatus rufinus (Merriam). Tawny Deer-mouse.

Reported at Abiquiu, Chama, Chama River, Española, Gallina, Gallinas Mountains, Jemez Mountains, Santa Clara Canyon, Taos, Taos Mountain, Taos Pueblo, Tierra Amarilla, and other localities in northern New Mexico, by Osgood.[3]

We collected one specimen above camp at El Rito de los Frijoles, which was identified by Mr. Warren.

Ŋwi̥·ŋ?

Peromyscus leucopus tornillo (Mearns). Tornillo Deer-mouse.

Reported at Santa Fe and other New Mexico localities, chiefly southwest of Santa Fe, by Osgood.[4]

Ŋwi̥·ŋ.

Peromyscus truei (Shufeldt). True's Deer-mouse.

Reported at Española, Gallinas Mountains, and other localities, by Osgood.[5]

This is the only species of white-footed deer-mouse common at El Rito de los Frijoles Canyon. The identity of our specimens was confirmed by Mr. Warren. The Indians thought the bluish-gray specimens were male and those with more ochraceous color were female, instead of being young and adult of each sex respectively.

---

[1] Goldman, Edward A., op. cit., pp. 56–58.

[2] Ibid., pp. 104–05.

[3] Osgood, Wilfred H., Revision of the Mice of the American Genus Peromyscus, *North American Fauna*, no. 28, Biol. Surv., U. S. Dept. Agr., pp. 72–74, 1909.

[4] Ibid., pp. 125–26.

[5] Ibid., pp. 165–69.

When questioned as to their habits the Indians said these mice "get young in the spring, the same as horses and cows, and give them milk just the same."

Ŋwiⁱŋ.
Mus musculus Linn.   Domestic Mouse.
Ŋwiⁱŋ.
Epimys norvegicus (Erxl.).   Domestic Rat.

It is said that there are no domestic rats in New Mexico. Domestic mice are as common in Indian houses as in those of Mexicans and Americans. These mice are called *ratones* in New Mexican Spanish.

'Ojo (? akin to Taos *pajanâ*, Isleta *patfare*, Castor canadensis frondator Mearns).
Castor canadensis frondator Mearns.   Broad-tailed Beaver.

The Tewa sometimes call the beaver *po"ojo*, 'water beaver' (*po*ʻ, water; *'ojo*, beaver).

Whites and Indians both report beaver along the Rio Grande, probably of this species; but the lateral canyons in the neighborhood of El Rito de los Frijoles support none now, if they ever did.

The beaver was hunted and eaten by the Tewa, and its use as food is said by them to have no ill effect.

? ———
Marmota flaviventer (Aud. & Bach).   Western Woodchuck.

None were seen and no information concerning them in our area was obtained. Reported at Santa Fe by Coues and Yarrow.[1]

Kiⁱ.
Cynomys gunnisoni (Baird).   Gunnison's Prairie Dog.

None found at El Rito de los Frijoles, but abundant at Valle Grande in the Jemez Mountains, just beyond the head of the ʻRito. The Indians report prairie dogs also at San Ildefonso and other points along the Rio Grande.

The bark of the *kiⁱ* is well imitated by Tewa men. They say: *kiⁱ nǫtu*, "the prairie dog speaks or gives his cry" (*kiⁱ*, Cynomys gunnisoni (Baird); *nǫ*, it; *tu*, to speak).

? ———
Citellus tridecemlineatus pallidus (Allen).   Striped Spermophile.

Citellus tridecemlineatus Mitch. was reported at Tierra Amarilla by Coues and Yarrow.[2] This record should probably be referred to the subspecies *pallidus*, which is found north of that locality in Colorado.

Soʻwæ.
Citellus grammurus (Say).   Rock Squirrel.

This large, speckled, bushy-tailed ground squirrel, its body a foot long, is abundant in the canyons about El Rito de los Frijoles. It is recognized by the Indians as a ground squirrel, with habits distinct

---

[1] Coues, Elliott, and Yarrow, H. C., op. cit., p. 123.   [2] Ibid., p. 120.

from those of tree squirrels. Three of them said that it sheds its hair in April and May, that the hair begins to thicken in July, and that late in August it gets "nice, warm hair, to fix up for the winter." The accuracy of some of the dates may be doubted. This ground squirrel damages their provisions. The Tewa eat the flesh, but do not use the skin.

Sǫ'wæ.
Callospermophilus lateralis (Say). Say's Ground Squirrel, "Big Chipmunk".

Common in the Jemez Mountains, about the headwaters of El Rito de los Frijoles, but not seen by us on the mesas or in the canyons which cut them. Easily recognized by lateral yellowish stripe and black stripe; it is smaller than pine squirrel. Said to be common throughout the mountains of northern New Mexico. Our Indian informants recognized the species, distinguishing it from the other squirrels by its appearance, its habits, and its habitat, though they gave them the same name. They say it is restricted to the mountains and correctly consider it a ground squirrel. It is used by them for food.

Kuwije.
Eutamias quadrivittatus (Say). Four-lined Colorado Chipmunk.

Abundant in the canyons, in the mountains, and along the edges at least of the mesas. The Indians use it for food and are quite familiar with its range and habits. Recognized by its small size and the alternating light and dark stripes on the back.

Sǫ'wæ.
Sciurus aberti Woodhouse. Abert's Tufted-ear Squirrel.

This is the finest squirrel of the region, as large as the rock squirrel, gray above, white beneath, with long and very bushy tail, its long leaps from tree to tree never failing to excite the utmost admiration. We found it only among the big rock pines on the mesas, where it is rather common. It was long ago reported at Santa Fe by Coues and Yarrow,[1] and from Santa Fe to Taos by Coues and Allen.[2] It is eaten by the Indians. The tufts of hair on the ears are called *'ojep'o,* 'ear hairs'.

Sǫ'wæ.
Sciurus fremonti Aud. & Bach. Fremont's Chickaree, "Pine Squirrel".

Abundant in the Jemez Mountains. Our Indians declared that it occurs only among the firs and spruces, a statement well founded but too sweeping. Although almost universally called "pine squirrel" in Colorado, it is found in various parts of that State much more commonly among the firs and spruces and not abundant among the rock pines. In New Mexico in ascending the canyon of El Rito de

---

[1] Coues, Elliott, and Yarrow, H. C., op. cit., p. 115.
[2] Coues, Elliott, and Allen, J. A., Monographs of North American Rodentia, *Final Rep. U. S. Geol. Surv. Terr.,* XI, pp. 737–38, 1877.

los Frijoles we encountered the first one where we first found firs, about 2 miles above the house of Judge Abbott, but he says it occasionally is seen downstream as far as his ranch. Allen [1] has described a subspecies (*Sciurus fremonti neomexicanus*) from the eastern slopes of the Taos Mountains in Colfax and Moro Counties, "very different from specimens from central and northern Colorado," but he records a specimen from Chama, which he refers to *fremonti*. Our specimens from the Jemez Mountains, collected in August, 1910, were found to be slightly redder than specimens taken in northwestern Colorado in August, 1909, but possibly the latter had faded a trifle. Though smaller than some others, this is the best food squirrel in the region.

Pọ·tse'ᵉ.
Lutra canadensis (Schreber). Canadian Otter.
Pọ·tse'ᵉ.
Lutra canadensis sonora Rhoads. Sonoran Otter.

Mr. Dowell, who has trapped extensively in the region, says the otter occurs along the Rio Grande near by. The Indians confirm this, and fragments of otter skin are worn by them. Without specimens for identification we can not know which form it is.

Je·.
? *Mustela arizonensis* Mearns. Mountain Weasel.

Weasels are reported at San Ildefonso by the Indians, but we have no specimens for identification. Coues and Yarrow [2] reported *Putorius longicauda* Merriam at Taos, but this region seems more likely to be within the range of *arizonensis*, much more recently described. *Mustela streatori leptus* Merriam may also extend into northern New Mexico.

Hodge gives *Dyé-tdoa* as "Gopher" clans of San Juan, Santa Clara, San Ildefonso, and Tesuque, and *Yé-tdóa* as "Lizard" clans of San Juan and San Ildefonso.

? ———

Lutreola vison energumenos Bangs. Western Mink.

Mr. Dowell says mink occur along the Rio Grande near El Rito de los Frijoles.

? ———

Martes caurina origenes (Rhoads). Rocky Mountain Marten.

Hodge states that Bandelier gives a "Marten" clan as existing at San Juan pueblo.

Coues and Yarrow [3] recorded *Mustela americana* Turton from Taos. That is a species of the north. It is likely the more recently described southern form.

---

[1] Allen, J. A., Revision of the Chickarees, or North American Red Squirrels (Subgenus Tamiasciurus), *Bull. Amer. Mus. Nat. Hist.*, x, pp. 291–94, 1898.
[2] Coues, Elliott, and Yarrow, H. C., op. cit., p. 59.
[3] Ibid., p. 61.

K̃e'a.

Taxidea taxus Schreber.   Badger.

Hodge gives as Badger clans of various pueblos: San Juan, *Kéya-tdóa;* Santa Clara, *Keä-tdóa;* San Ildefonso, *Kéa-tdoa;* Jemez, *Son-saásh;* Pecos, *So'hl+;* Laguna, *Chópï-hánoᶜʰ;* Sia, *Tyúpi-háno;* Zuñi, *Tónashi-kwe.*

We found no badgers nor their holes at El Rito de los Frijoles, and could learn of none. At the old Buckman sawmill, at the base of the Jemez Mountains, we chased two into their hole, but did not get them. Two of the Indians told, with much glee, of the fighting qualities of this animal and its great energy in digging. They told also of how a badger caught one of them by the trousers and held on until it was dragged a long distance to the river and into the water.

Sǫ̆'.

Mephitis mesomelas varians Gray.   Long-tailed Texas Skunk.

The Indians report striped skunks at San Ildefonso, which appears to be within the probable range of this species. We learned of no spotted skunks, though the region is between the known range of the Rocky Mountain species (*Spilogale tenuis* Howell) and that of the Great Basin species (*Spilogale gracilis saxatilis* Merriam), so one or the other probably occurs within our area. Skunk skins are used by the Tewa for ceremonial purposes.

Ke· (akin to Taos *köaanâ,* Isleta *köaire,* bear).

Bear (any species).

Ursus horribilis Ord.   Grizzly Bear.

Ursus horribilis horrixæus Baird.   Sonora Grizzly.

Ursus americanus Pallas.   Black Bear.

The Jemez name is *ɾwǎlǫ̆;* the Cochiti name is *kóhaju,* the Hopi name *hónaù'ɯ.*

Hodge gives as Bear clans at various pueblos: San Juan and Nambe, *Ke-tdóa;* Hano, *Ké-tówa;* Pecos, *Whalatdásh;* Acoma, *Küwhaía-hánoqᶜʰ;* Sia, *Kohaí-háno;* San Felipe, *Kóhai-háno;* Cochiti, *Kúhaia-hánuch;* Zuñi, *Aíñshi-kwe.*

As is usually the case, the hunters interviewed, white as well as Indian, were not sufficiently familiar with the species of bear to give definite information. Whites talked about black, brown, and cinnamon bears, all of which refer to color phases of the black bear, which is not at all uncommon in the region. We occasionally saw bear tracks. The Indians vaguely described five kinds of bear: *ke· tsæ·'i'i hehæñu'i'i,* 'big white bear' (*ke·,* bear; *tsæ·,* white; *hehæñu,* big); *ke· tsæ·'i'i tʃæ·'i'i,* 'little white bear' (*ke·,* bear; *tsæ·,* white; *tʃæ·,* little); *ke· tse·jì'ⁱ,* 'yellow bear' (*ke·,* bear; *tse·,* yellow); *ke· 'ǫ̆wì'ⁱ,* 'brown bear' (*ke·,* bear; *'ǫ̆,* brown); *ke· p'ę·ŋdi'ⁱ,* 'black bear' (*ke·,* bear; *p'ę·ŋ,* black).

As this region is within the range of the grizzly, the "white bear" may refer to either *horribilis* or its subspecies *horrixæus,* more likely the former. It is notable that Lewis and Clark and other early explorers in the West called the grizzly the white bear. It is to be noted that there is but one Indian name for the bear, in spite of the fact that they describe five kinds, a nomenclature paralleled in many other languages of the Southwest. Bandelier [1] says in his Final Report:

The bear makes great havoc among the piñon trees. Climbing into the tops for the nuts, he tears off entire limbs and generally ruins the tree. Three kinds of bears are spoken of by the Indians and the Spanish settlers: The silver-tip (Platiado, Ko-ha-yo Kash-ya), the brown bear (Oso colorado, Ko-ha-yo Ke-han-ye), and the black bear (Oso prieto, Ko-ha-yo Moh'-na-ka-nyi).

Bandelier doubted the identity of the "silver-tip" with the grizzly, because he did not believe the latter species was found in this area. The Indian word-forms quoted are presumably in the Cochiti dialect of the Keres language.

Po·musà, 'water cat' (*po·*, water; *musà*, house cat). See *musà*, page 29.

Procyon lotor Linn. Raccoon.

The "coon" is said to occur in the Rio Grande Canyon, near the mouth of El Rito de los Frijoles and elsewhere. Russell [2] gives *va'owŏk* as the Pima name for this species, and says:

The raccoon is said to be used for food, though the writer did not see any of the animals or any of their skins during a stay of a year and a half in Arizona.

Tse (akin to Taos *tsulanâ*, dog).

Domestic Dog.

The Isleta call the dog *qwianiʌe*, the Jemez *kⁱânù*, the Hopi *pokò*, the Zuñi *wátsita*.

There is some direct and much indirect evidence that domesticated dogs were widely distributed among the North American Indians before the landing of Columbus. The fact that all Indian languages which have come to our attention contain native names for the dog, distinct from that applied to the coyote, wolf, and fox, is significant. No less significant is the fact that the names for the horse and other animals introduced by the whites are either newly coined words of descriptive meaning, modifications of the names for some other animal, or adaptations of the names used by white men. The Indians of the Southwest, including the Pueblos, are not exceptions. They have native names for the dog, while their names for the horse are either descriptive, compound, or derived from the Spanish. Possibly an examination of early Spanish documents relating to the Southwest would develop direct statements in regard to dogs found in possession of the natives at their earliest contact with the whites, but lack of present access to the literature as well as lack of time prevent us from going far into the subject.

[1] Bandelier, A. F., op. cit., p. 150, note.
[2] Russell, Frank, The Pima Indians, *Twenty-sixth Ann. Rep. Bur. Amer. Ethn.*, p. 82, 1908.

The hairless dogs of Mexico, Peru, and South America, of several kinds, existed there when the Spaniards landed, according to various accounts.[1] All Peruvian dogs are said to have been derived from the Inca shepherd dog.[2] The Eskimo dog was described as early as 1647, and in various parts of the north polar region, races or tribes have developed quite different systems of calls for the direction of their dog teams, indicating long use.[3] The Flatheads,[4] Menomini,[5] and many other Indians mention dogs in their myths, but unless we know the age of the myths, which may have incorporated references to the dog after the invasion of the whites, they are of little value in this connection. The Pima have a myth giving the origin of the horse,[6] which was surely introduced. However, it is not likely that such a myth as the white dog and woman myth[7] could be so widespread unless very ancient.

McGee[8] says:

It is significant that the Dakota word for horse (*šuk-tañ'-ka* or *šuη-ka'-wa-kaη*) is composed of the word for dog (*šuη'-ka*), with an affix indicating greatness, sacredness or mystery . . . and that several terms for harness and other appurtenances correspond with those used for the gear of the dog when used as a draft animal. This terminology corroborates the direct evidence that the dog was domesticated by the Siouan aborigines long before the advent of the horse.

Bones of dogs have been reported from the ancient kitchen-middens of the Atlantic coast, and bones of other animals apparently bearing the tooth-marks of dogs.[9]

The De Soto expedition in 1539–1542, within half a century after the landing of Columbus, at an Indian village in the mountains of Georgia or South Carolina was "welcomed in a friendly manner, the Indians giving them a little corn and many wild turkeys, together with some dogs of a peculiar small species, which were bred for eating purposes and did not bark."[10]

In the reports of the Coronado expedition to the Southwest from 1540 to 1542, the same period covered by De Soto in the Southeast, dogs were reported in abundant use as beasts of burden by the Indians of the Staked Plains and elsewhere.[11]

---

[1] Lockington, W. N., The Riverside Natural History, article on Carnivoræ.
[2] Brinton, Daniel G., The American Race, p. 212, 1891.
[3] Langkavel, B., Dogs and Savages, *Smithsonian Rep. for 1898*, p. 659–60, 1899.
[4] Ibid., p. 651.
[5] Hoffman, Walter James, The Menomini Indians, *Fourteenth Ann. Rep. Bur. Amer. Ethn.*, pt. I, pp. 179–194, 1896.
[6] Russell, Frank, The Pima Indians, *Twenty-sixth Ann. Rep. Bur. Amer. Ethn.*, p. 241, 1908.
[7] Dorsey, George A., and Kroeber, Alfred L., Traditions of the Arapaho, *Pub. no. 81, Field Columbian Museum*, V, pp. 207–09, 1903.
[8] McGee, W J, Siouan Indians, *Fifteenth Ann. Rep. Bur. Amer. Ethn.*, p. 174, 1897.
[9] Marquis de Nadaillac, Pre-historic America, pp. 49–50, 535, 1895.
[10] Mooney, James, Myths of the Cherokee, *Nineteenth Ann. Rep. Bur. Amer. Ethn.*, pt. I, p. 25, 1900 (quoting Ranjel).
[11] Langkavel, B., op. cit., p. 661. Winship, George Parker, The Coronado Expedition, 1540–1542, *Fourteenth Ann. Rep. Bur. Amer. Ethn.*, pt. I, pp. 401, 405, 504, 507, 527, 570, 578, 1896.

Fewkes [1] reports:

The ancient Hopi had a domestic dog which was a pet rather than a beast of burden. The good qualities of this ⁻et were recognized and recounted in their legends.

Russell [2] says:

The only domesticated animal which there is any certainty that the Pimas possessed at the time of the discovery is the dog. The old people say that in their youth the dogs were all alike and resembled coyotes. At present there are many small mongrels, obtained principally from the Mexicans.

Hough [3] says that "remains of the dog and turkey were found in nearly every ruin" in northeastern Arizona.

Fewkes, in his account of certain Arizona ruins, [4] says:

The occurrence of a skull of the domesticated dog in one of the graves at the Chaves Pass ruin is significant, showing that this animal was known to the ancients, and probably utilized by them. The fact that this dog was the broad-faced variety is particularly instructive. It was not apparently a domesticated coyote or a mongrel like those which now are so common in some of the pueblos.

Lucas [5] gives the following account of this skull:

Among the many objects obtained by Dr. Fewkes last summer from the ruined pueblo of Chaves Pass, Arizona, is the cranium of a domesticated dog, found in a grave with a human skeleton. Although the mere fact of a dog being discovered under such circumstances is in itself interesting, it is not at first sight remarkable, since it is well known that in America, as elsewhere, the dog was domesticated at an early date, and Clavijero mentions an ancient dog which he calls "a quadruped of the country of Cibola, similar in form to a mastiff, which the Indians employ to carry burdens." Aside from the fact that this is the first dog's cranium discovered by Dr. Fewkes, there are some points of special interest in the present case. Most of the Indian dogs are more or less wolfish in their aspect, and have long skulls, with comparatively low foreheads, thus showing a small degree of specialization in the way of breed, and this is true of such of the mummied dogs of Egypt as I have seen. The cranium of the Chaves dog, on the contrary, is of the broad-faced type, with high forehead, and, curiously enough, is precisely similar in size and proportions to the cranium of an Eskimo dog from Cumberland Sound, the resemblance extending to the peculiar concavity and squareness of the nasal region. While this is an interesting coincidence, it is not brought forward as implying community of origin, but as instancing long domestication in order that so well-marked a breed could be established. A curious confirmation of the early origin of this breed was received from San Marcos, Texas, where, in excavating for ponds, at the station of the U. S. Fish Commission, a human skeleton and bones of other animals were found in a layer containing many flint implements, overlaid by two feet of black soil. The bones were those of existing species, including teeth of several bison, and there was also a fragment of a dog's skull similar in size and proportions to that obtained at Chaves Pass.

From the apparent general distribution of the dog, an animal particularly useful to primitive people throughout North America at a

[1] Fewkes, J. Walter, Property-right in Eagles Among the Hopi, *Amer. Anthr.*, n. s., II, p. 706, 1900.
[2] Russell, Frank, op. cit., p. 84.
[3] Hough, Walter, Archæological Field Work in Northeastern Arizona: The Museum-Gates Expedition of 1901, *Ann. Rep. U. S. Nat. Museum for 1901*, pp. 316, 326, 339, 356, 1903.
[4] Fewkes, Jesse Walter, Two Summers' Work in Pueblo Ruins, *Twenty-second Ann. Rep. Bur. Amer. Ethn.*, pt. I, p. 27, 1904.
[5] Lucas, F. A., A Dog of the Ancient Pueblos, *Science*, n. s., V, p. 544, 1897.

remote period, together with the existence of native names for dogs in the Pueblo dialects, it is practically certain that the ancient dwellers in the region had domesticated dogs. The difficulty of distinguishing the bones of some of the native dogs from those of the coyote has been emphasized by Coues.[1] Cross-breeding with various European dogs since the advent of the whites, in addition to cross-breeding with coyotes and possibly with wolves, has developed a mixed race which makes the subject a difficult one to study now. We have noticed the frequent occurrence of a yellowish short-haired variety of dog at San Juan pueblo.

The Tewa give names of most varied meaning to their dogs. One dog at Santa Clara pueblo is named *puꞏ'eꞏ*, "little jackrabbit."

Tewa dogs are apt to lie in the outdoor adobe ovens, when these are not in use, if the openings are not closed in some way.

Tsinì (?<Span. *chino*).   Curly-haired Dog.

The word *tsinì* puzzled us much. It was said to refer to a kind of small dog which the Tewa had in primitive times. Investigation showed that the word usually applies to a curly-haired dog, small or large. In New Mexican Spanish *chino* applies to a curly-haired dog. So far as we know, Spanish-English dictionaries do not give *chino* with this meaning. Guinn,[2] however, mentions this usage of *chino* in southern California: "Chino, while it does mean a Chinaman, is also applied in Spanish-American countries to persons or animals having curly hair." The final *i* of the Tewa form, instead of *ù*, is unexplained.

Ḍeꞏ.
Canis estor Merriam.   Coyote.

In Tewa mythology the coyote is called also *poseqwaseꞏŋḍoꞏ*, a word which can not be etymologized except that the last two syllables mean 'old man.'

The Jemez name meaning 'coyote' is *ją́ꞏ*. In Cochiti Keresan 'coyote' is called *ʃótsona*.

Coyote tracks are common all over the region. A coyote taken by Mr. Dowell while we were in the Rito de los Frijoles canyon is referred to this species.

Hodge gives as Coyote clans of various pueblos: San Juan, San Ildefonso, and Tesuque, *Dé-tdóa;* Jemez, *Yaⁿtsaá;* Pecos, *Ya'+;* Laguna, *Tsŭshki-hánoᶜʰ;* Sia, *Shútsun'-háno;* San Felipe, *Shrótsona-háno;* Santa Ana, *Shutsón-háno;* Cochiti, *Shrútsuna-hánuch;* Zuñi, *Súski-kwe.*

Kꞏụ̀ꞏ'joꞏ (akin to Taos *kalenâ*, Isleta *kariɹè*, wolf).
Canis nubilis Say.   Gray Wolf.

---

[1] Coues, Elliott, The Prairie Wolf, or Coyoté: Canis Latrans, *Amer. Nat.*, VII, pp. 385–89, 1873; reprinted in Coues and Yarrow, Report upon Collections of Mammals, etc., op. cit., pp. 47–51.

[2] Guinn, J. M., Historical and Biographical Record of Southern California, Chicago, 1902, p. 59.

Gatschet [1] gives Tewa "kōyo" erroneously as meaning coyote and compares it with Nahua *coyotl*.

Hodge gives as Wolf clans of pueblos: Isleta, *Túim-t'aínïn;* Laguna, *Kákhan-hano^{ch}*.

The Tewa say that the gray wolf is very scarce now, but is still occasionally seen in the Taos mountains. It is common in many portions of New Mexico and is reported at Taos by Bailey.[2]

Mu̦·jo·.

?Red fox.

The Tewa are familiar with a foxlike animal called *mu̦·jo·*, although they say it is seldom seen. It is said to resemble the *de· tsą̆·ŋwæ·"i'i* (see below), but is of a dark brownish-yellow color.

De· tsą̆·ŋwæ·"i'i, 'blue coyote' (*de·*, coyote; *tsą̆·ŋwæ·*, blue, green). *Urocyon cinereoargenteus scotti* Mearns. Scott's Gray Fox, Piñon Fox.

Coues and Yarrow [3] recorded *Urocyon cinereo-argentateus* Schreber from Taos, but the specimen was more likely *scotti*, a species more recently described. Mr. Nathan Dowell reports both the gray and the red fox at El Rito de los Frijoles, but we can not know just what species without specimens for identification.

K'æ·ŋîsæ·, 'white mountain lion' (*k'æ·ŋ*, mountain lion; *îsæ·*, white).

Any kind of wildcat.

The Southern Ute also have only one word for wildcat species: *mosútukwïtsï*. The Southern Ute word meaning 'medicine man' appears to be related: *mosútukwïätö*.

The Tewa name may apply to a species of bobcat or lynx or perhaps to both a species of bobcat and a species of lynx. The informants did not know the characters by which the bobcat and lynx are distinguished. We saw no *k'æ·ŋîsæ·*, but saw the tracks of one near the Painted Cave. It is likely that either *baileyi* or *uinta* would be found here, perhaps both, the former being an animal of the plains and the latter a mountain-loving animal.

The name shows that this animal is closely associated with the mountain lion in the minds of the Tewa.

Musà.

Domestic Cat.

This word in this or similar form appears in most of the languages of the Southwest, meaning introduced house cat. Compare also Tewa *po·musà*, raccoon.

---

[1] Zwölf Sprachen aus dem Südwesten Nordamerikas, Weimar, 1876, p. 26.
[2] Bailey, Vernon, Wolves in Relation to Stock, Game, and the National Forest Reserves, *Bull. No. 72, Forest Service, U. S. Dept. Agr.*, p. 12, 1907; Destruction of Wolves and Coyotes, *Circular No. 63, Biol. Surv., U. S. Dept. Agr.*, p. 6, 1908.
[3] Op. cit., Wheeler Survey, v, p. 56.

House cats of many varieties are common at the Tewa pueblos. They are called to: '*musà, musà, musà.*' They are sometimes given proper names, as dogs are.

> *K'ǽ·ŋ* (akin to Isleta *k'imiⱡè*, mountain lion).
> *Felis hippolestes* Merriam. Rocky Mountain Cougar, Puma, Mountain Lion.

The Southern Ute name for mountain lion is *toku.*

The mountain lion is reported for this region by both whites and Indians. The Tewa say that the animal crouches or sits waiting for its prey. The carved figures of the "Stone Lions" shrine on the Pajarito plateau are identified by the Tewa as *k'ǽ·ŋ*, and the name of that place in the Tewa language is *k'ǽ·ŋɖa'ǽ·ŋɖìwè*, 'where the two mountain lions crouch' (*k'ǽ·ŋ*, mountain lion; *ɖa*, they two; '*ǽ·ŋ*, to sit, to crouch; '*iwe*, locative).

Hodge gives as Mountain Lion clans of various pueblos: San Juan and San Ildefonso, *Kän-tdóa;* Nambe, *Që-tdóa;* Isleta, *Kim-t'ainïn;* Pecos, *Shiañk'yá+;* Laguna, *Mókaiqch-hánoᶜʰ;* Sia and San Felipe, *Mókaich-háno;* Cochiti, *Móhkach-hánuch.*

> *K'ǽ·ŋ.*
> *Siⱡkùk'ǽ·ŋ* (*siⱡkù*, circus, <Span. *circo; k'ǽ·ŋ*, mountain lion, lion).
> Lion.
> *Ną̀·ŋk'ǽ·ŋ*, 'earth mountain lion' (*ną̀·ŋ*, earth; *k'ǽ·ŋ*, mountain lion).
> ? ———

Whether the animal thus called is mythic or real has not been determined. It is the sacred beast of the nadir. It is said to be a small animal which burrows in the earth. It is not the pocket-gopher, which is called *tʃugì.* We have no record of shrews or moles.

> *Kwǽ·ji* (? <Span. *caballo*).
> *Kaɓajù* (<Span. *caballo*).
> Domestic Horse.

The Tewa apply both *kwǽ·ji* and *kaɓajù* to any kind of horse, but use the former term when they talk about horses in the presence of a Mexican and fear that *kaɓajù* will be understood. It is possible that both *kwǽ·ji* and *kaɓajù* are borrowed from Spanish *caballo,* the former being an earlier, the latter a later borrowing.

For female horse *jewà* (<Span. *yegua*) seems to be the common term, though *kaɓajùkwi·*, 'horse female' (*kaɓajù*, horse; *kwi·*, female) is also in use. For young female horses *jewità* (<Span. *yeguita*) and *potaŋkà* (<Span. *potranca*) are heard; young male horses are called *potrijù* (<Span. *potrillo*). A stallion is regularly called *gaⱡañuŋ* (<Span. *garañon*).

Many of the Indian languages of the Southwest have, like Tewa,. borrowed the Spanish word *caballo* as a designation for the horse. In Southern Ute the horse is mostly called *pukútsi*, a term which seems to have originally meant 'pet.' But *kaƀajù* (<Span. *caballo*) is also used.

The Tewa now use horses in the same way as the Mexicans who live in their country. The Tewa frequently go to the Jicarilla Apache country to buy horses. The Jicarilla Apache are noted for their fine horses, which they sell cheap.

There are wild horses to be found on the mesa south of Buckman,. N. Mex.

> *Ḅuḍù* (<Span. *burro*).
> *'Ojeso'jo''e'*, 'big-eared little animal' (*'oje*, ear; *so'jo'*, big; *'e'*, diminutive).
> Domestic Donkey.

It is said that when donkeys first became known to the Tewa the term *'ojeso'jo''e'* alone was used. This term is still employed by the Tewa when talking in the presence of Mexicans, lest they understand the word *ḅuḍù*.

The Hopi corruption of Spanish *burro* is *моло;* cf. Voth's "móro." [1]
A donkey stallion is called *ḅuḍù gaлañuŋ* (<Span. *burro garañon*).

> *Matʃù* (<Span. *macho*).
> *'Ojeso'jo''e'*, 'big-eared little animal' (*'oje*, ear; *so'jo'*, big; *'e'*, diminutive).
> Mule.

The male mule is called *matʃù* (<Span. *macho*), the female mule is called *mulà* (<Span. *mula*). Young mules are called *matʃù'e'* or *mulà'e'*, *'e'* being the diminutive.

'Ojeso'jo''e' seems to be rarely applied to mules.
The Tewa do not own as many mules as they own horses and donkeys.

> *Seḅà* (<Span. *zebra*).
> Zebra.

> *Hiлap'à* (<Span. *jirafa*).
> *Ke ḍugì'ⁱ*, 'long neck' (*ke*, neck; *ḍugì*, long).
> Giraffe.

> *Kamejù* (<Span. *camello*).
> Camel.

> *Wa·sì*.
> Cattle, Cow.

---

1 Voth, Hopi Proper Names, *Field Columbian Museum Publications, Anthr. Ser.*, VI, no. 3, p. 113, 1905.

The San Ildefonso, Nambe, and San Juan dialects have *wa·sì;* the Tesuque and Santa Clara dialects *wa·gà.* The Hano Tewa name is unknown. Both *wa·sì* and *wa·gà* may be adapted from Navaho *wégaʃi,* 'cow,' or *wa·sì* may come from Navaho *wégaʃi* and *wa·gà* directly from Spanish *vaca.* The Franciscan fathers [1] give Navaho "bĕgashi" as derived from Spanish *vaca* (in their spelling *vacca* or *bacca,* influenced by Latin *vacca?*) plus an element "*shi.*" The Zuñi name is *wákashi.*

A milch cow is called *wa·p̂o·wa·sì* (*wa·*, breast; *p̂o·*, water; *wa·sì*, cow) or *wa·p̂o·wa·gà* (*wa·*, breast; *p̂o·*, water; *wa·gà*, cow). A castrated ox or steer is called *wejè* (<Span. *buey*), and a bull *tǫd̦ù* (<Span. *toro*). To use *wa·sìsę·ŋ,* 'male cow' (*wa·sì*, cow; *sę·ŋ*, male) is likely to make a Tewa smile. The young of the species is designated by adding the diminutive *'e·* to *wa·sì, wa·gà, wejè, tǫd̦ù,* etc. Dehorned cattle are frequently called *pelụŋ* (<Span. *pelon*).

The Tewa keep a considerable number of cattle and use the milk as well as the flesh and other products. Women usually do the milking. Cattle dung (*wa·sìsa·* or *wagàsa·*) is considered the superior sort for kneading into the cakes used in firing pottery.

Petsuʌe.
Swine.
This word is applied to either sex of swine, or the ordinary sex-age elements may be added. Tewa *petsuʌe* is possibly borrowed from or at least of the same origin as Navaho "bisódĕ," 'swine'.[2] The Franciscan fathers say of the swine: "It was most likely first brought to their (i. e., the Navahos') country from Old Mexico, as the name, bisódĕ, a corruption of the Aztec pitsotl, seems to indicate." None of the common New Mexican Spanish words for swine (*marrano, cochino, puerco, marrana, cochina, puerca*) is used much in Tewa speech.

The Tewa keep a few swine in sties and are very fond of the flesh.

'Elep'aŋtè (<Span. *elefante*).
Elephant.
The trunk of the elephant is called simply *ʃu,* 'nose'.

Ŋwi̦·ŋ t͡sæ·'i'i, 'white rat,' (*ŋwi̦·ŋ*, rat, mouse; *t͡sæ·*, white).
Domestic White Rat.
One of our informants knew of these animals and their use as pets.

[1] Franciscan Fathers, Ethnologic Dictionary of the Navaho Language, St. Michaels, Ariz., 1910, p. 143.
[2] Ibid., p. 142.

BIRDS[1]

'Oᵬį.

Duck.

The Tewa have only this one name for species of wild duck; it is also applied to the domestic duck, which has been introduced to some extent among them. Descriptive terms may of course be added to designate definite species or individual ducks.

The Taos call duck *papiânâ*, the Isleta *p̂apiɹe*. The Jemez name meaning duck is *wǎʃiʃi*.

Hodge gives *Waíushr-háno* as a Duck clan of San Felipe.

A number of species of duck surely occur in this region during migration, but we have no definite record.

Ḳạgì.

Branta canadensis canadensis (Linn.). Canada Goose.

The Tewa have apparently only one name for species of wild goose and this they apply also to the domestic goose.

Hodge gives *Kúnni-t'aínin* as a Goose clan of Isleta.

McCall[2] says: "I did not meet the Canada goose until I reached the Rio Grande, which was at a point 60 miles below El Paso; thence I found them tolerably numerous until I left the river near Santa Fe." He also reports as occasional the snow goose (*Chen hyperborcus hyperboreus* [Pallas]), white-fronted goose (*Anser albifrons gambeli* Hartlaub), and the brant (*Bernicla brenta* Steph. = *Branta bernicla glaucogastra* [Brehm]) along the Rio Grande, but does not indicate how far north he saw them. Other species doubtless occur, including the whistling and trumpeter swans, but we have no records.

? *Grus canadensis* (Linn.). Little Brown Crane.

McCall[2] found this crane on the Rio Grande from Santa Fe to El Paso in October, more abundant below Albuquerque.

To·tæ·ᵬì, apparently 'sagebrush softness' (*to·*, Rocky Mountain sagebrush; *tæ·ᵬì*, softness, soft). The Santa Clara say merely *ío·tæ·*.

Callipepla squamata squamata (Vigors). Scaled Quail.

Judge Abbott and Mr. Dowell say that large flocks sometimes visit the Rito de los Frijoles.

---

[1] For comparative purposes consult the following: Henshaw, H. W., Report upon the Ornithological Collections made in Portions of Nevada, Utah, California, Colorado, New Mexico, and Arizona during the years 1871, 1872, 1873, and 1874, *U. S. Geog. Explor. & Surv. W. of 100th Merid.*, v, pp. 131–507, 1875. Henshaw, H. W., and Nelson, E. W., List of Birds Observed in Summer and Fall on the Upper Pecos River, New Mexico, *The Auk*, II, pp. 326–33, 1885; III, pp. 73–80, 1886. Gilman, M. French, Birds on the Navajo Reservation in New Mexico, *The Condor*, X, pp. 146–52, 1908. Mitchell, Walton I., The Summer Birds of San Miguel County, New Mexico, *The Auk*, XV, pp. 306–11, 1898. Bailey, Florence Merriam, Additional Notes on the Birds of the Upper Pecos, ibid., XXI, pp. 349–63, 1904; Additions to Mitchell's List of the Summer Birds of San Miguel County, New Mexico, ibid., pp. 443–49. Henry, T. Charlton, Catalogue of the Birds of New Mexico as Compiled from Notes and Observations Made While in that Territory, During a Residence of Six Years, *Proc. Acad. Nat. Sci. Phila.*, 1859, XI, pp. 104–09, 1860.

[2] McCall, George A., Some Remarks on the Habits, etc., of Birds Met with in Western Texas, Between San Antonio and the Rio Grande, and in New Mexico, etc., ibid., v, p. 223, 1852.

'ʃæ·'.

Dendragapus obscurus obscurus (Say).   Dusky Grouse.

The informants' description of ʃæ· fits this species well.   This large grouse is common in the Jemez Mountains and is said to come down into the canyons about El Rito de los Frijoles in large numbers in the autumn.   It is one of the important food birds of the region and is probably to be found breeding in all the mountains of north-central New Mexico.   A few flocks were seen by McCall in the mountains from Santa Fe to Taos.[1]

? ———

Lagopus leucurus leucurus (Swainson).   White-tailed Ptarmigan.

Under the name *Lagopus leucurus altipetens* Osgood this bird has been reported in the Pecos Mountains and the mountains about Taos,[2] but that form is considered indistinguishable from *leucurus*. The species has been reported from Summit Peak, Colo., west of the Rio Grande,[3] so that it may occur on the western side of the valley in New Mexico.   The ptarmigan is a bird of high latitude and high altitude, preferring the region of perpetual snow.   It is exceedingly probable that during the latter part of the glacial epoch, when glaciers extended down most of the upper mountain valleys of Colorado and northern New Mexico, the snow-line was much lower, and the regular range of the ptarmigan, leucosticte, and other birds of alpine habit extended to elevations perhaps several thousand feet lower than at present, and probably considerably farther south.   By the retreat of the glaciers their range has been gradually restricted so that now only a few are left on the higher peaks.   It is likely that the ptarmigan was known to the ancient inhabitants of the Pajarito Plateau, and it may have occurred in considerable numbers at the head of the Rito, especially during the winter, 10 or 20 centuries ago.

? ———

Centrocercus urophasianus (Bonaparte).   Sage Hen.

Reported at Tierra Amarilla by Henshaw.[4]   Parts of the Rio Grande Valley are well suited to this bird.   If it formerly occurred in numbers, its large size would have made it an important addition to the diet of the inhabitants.

Ḍi· (akin to Isleta *diʌuʌe*).

P̂į·ŋḍi· (*p̂į·ŋ*, mountain; *ḍi·*, turkey, chicken).

Meleagris gallopavo merriami Nelson.   Merriam's Turkey.

The uncompounded *ḍi·* is now applied mostly to the introduced domestic fowl or chicken and not to turkey as it doubtlessly was formerly.   *P̂į·ŋ*, 'mountain,' is usually prejoined to distinguish turkeys

[1] McCall, George A., op. cit., p. 222.

[2] Bailey, Florence Merriam, Notes from Northern New Mexico, *The Auk*, XXII, pp. 316–18, 1905.   Additional Notes on the Birds of the Upper Pecos, ibid., XXI, pp. 351–52, 1904.

[3] Henshaw, H. W., Note on Lagopus leucurus and Leucosticte australis, *The Auk*, XXII, pp. 315–16, 1905.

[4] Henshaw, H. W., Report upon Ornithological Collections, etc., op. cit., p. 437.

from chickens. *Ḍi·* or *p̣i·ŋḍi·* applies to the domestic as well as to the
wild turkey. The Isleta terms meaning 'turkey' exactly parallel the
Tewa, *diⱮuⱮe* being the equivalent of Tewa *ḍi·*, and *p̂iendiⱮuⱮe* that of
Tewa *p̣i·ŋḍi·*. The Cochiti call turkey *tséna.*

Hodge gives as Turkey clans of various pueblos: Pecos, *P'etdelŭ'+*;
Laguna, *Tsï'na-háno*[ch]; Acoma, *Tsína-hánoq*[ch]; Sia, *Tsï-háno;* San
Felipe, *Tsína-háno;* Santa Ana, *Tsínha-háno;* Cochiti, *Tsï'n-hano;*
Zuñi, *Tóna-kwe.*

The Mexicans in New Mexico usually call the turkey *gallo de la
tierra, gallina de la tierra.* Spanish *guajalote* is not applied to the
turkey in New Mexico.

Turkeys breed in considerable numbers in the mountains. We
saw 30 in one flock at the edge of Valle Grande, just beyond the
headwaters of El Rito de los Frijoles. They come down into the
canyons in the autumn in large numbers and congregate about
the springs, where, it is said, they are slaughtered by the Mexicans.
There is no doubt that they were formerly much more abundant
than now and probably constituted an important article of food of
the ancient inhabitants. The Indians long ago domesticated this
bird, or, at any rate, kept many of them in inclosures. It is supposed that the birds in capitivity were kept for ceremonial purposes,
the feathers being used in various rites. This raises some doubt as
to whether the captive birds were used also for food. One of the
old men from Santa Clara pueblo said that the turkey is always
silent, "never makes any noise." This shows a surprising lack of
knowledge of the species. According to McCall,[1] 60 years ago it
"was found on almost every stream margined with timber, throughout the whole of the country traversed."

Ḍi·.
Domestic fowl, Chicken.

The name was originally applied to the wild turkey; see above.

The cock or rooster is called either *ḍi·sę·ŋ*, 'male chicken' (*ḍi·*,
chicken; *sę·ŋ*, male) or *gajù* (<Span. *gallo*).

The Tewa keep many chickens, and use the eggs (*ḍi·wa·*), flesh, and
feathers.

Ḳo'ǫŋwi·.
Zenaidura macroura marginella (Woodhouse). Western Mourning Dove.

The Taos name is *p̂iângaipaanâ;* Isleta, *ḳaipaiⱮe;* Jemez, *giŋǫmu.*

This dove was found to be abundant both in the canyons and on
the mesas. It is the only dovelike bird of the region, unless the
band-tailed pigeon occurs in limited numbers locally. The latter
may be recognized by the white nape band at the back of the skull

---

[1] McCall, George A., op. cit., p. 222.

of the male and of most females. The mourning dove is used for
food by the Indians. Our San Ildefonso Indian informants described
minutely the whistling of its wings and its call notes, which one of
the informants rendered by 'o—'o—'o—'o. When this imitation was
heard one of the old Indians broke out into a "rain song," which led
us to suspect that this bird was connected in his mind with rain.

Hodge gives as Dove clans of various pueblos: Sia, *Hóhoka-háno;*
San Felipe, *Húuka-háno;* Santa Ana, *Hóoka-háno.*

'Okǫ́wǫ.

Cathartes aura septentrionalis Wied.   Turkey Vulture.

We saw three in the Jemez Mountains, at the edge of the Valle
Grande, and one at Rito de los Frijoles Canyon. Our Indian informants said that this bird is confined to the mountains, lives on dead
meat, does not catch animals alive, and has a red head with no *p'o,*
'hair,' 'feathers,' on it. The Tewa did not eat the *'okǫ́wǫ.* They
were shown pictures of this vulture and of the California vulture or
condor (*Gymnogyps californianus* [Shaw]), and one old man who had
been in California at once pointed to the latter and exclaimed,
kalip'oɹnià'okǫ́wǫ, 'California vulture.'

Qwǫ·ɲpi·, 'red tail' (*qwǫ·ɲ,* tail; *pi·,* red).

Buteo borealis calurus Cassin.   Western Redtail.

This large hawk is fairly common all over the plateau. A pair
nested near camp at the Rito. The Indians recognize it by the color
of the tail and the screaming call note. They do not eat it. It is
probable that Swainson's hawk (*Buteo swainsoni* Bonaparte) is also
common, but we identified none with certainty.

Besides the *qwǫ·ɲpi·* the Tewa have names for three other kinds
of hawk. *Tʃugǫ* is the kind of hawk which the Mexicans call *gavilan.*
The *tʃugǫ* is said to be a large bird. *Qwǫ·ɲt'ɥ·,* 'spotted tail' (*qwǫ·ɲ,*
tail; *t'ɥ·,* spotted) is called by the Mexicans *cola pinta,* these words
having the same meaning.

The *qwǫ·ɲt'ɥ·* is smaller than the *tʃugǫ.* *Tiɲ* is the smallest species
of hawk known to the Tewa and is of the color of a *jɥ·ɲ,* 'mockingbird.'

Hodge gives *Kyuⁿgäⁿ-tdóa* as a Hawk clan of San Ildefonso.

Tse·.

Eagle.

Haliæetus leucocephalus leucocephalus (Linn.).   Bald Eagle.

Eagles of various colors are mentioned in Tewa mythology. *Tse·*
is the *tsiɹetujo,* 'chieftain bird' (*tsiɹe,* bird; *tujo,* chieftain), and
symbolizes the zenith in the beast-identifications of the world-
regions. The Isleta call eagle *ʃuiɹe;* the Cochiti, *t'áme;* the Hopi,
kwahu.

Hodge gives as Eagle clans of various pueblos: San Juan (given by

Bandelier), Santa Clara, and Tesuque, *Tse-tdóa;* San Ildefonso and Nambe, *Tsë-tdóa;* Isleta, *Shíu-t'ainïn;* Jemez, *Sehtsa-ásh;* Pecos, *Seé+;* Laguna, *Tyámi-háno^ch;* Acoma, *T'yámï-hánoq^ch;* Sia, San Felipe, and Santa Ana, *D'yámi-háno;* Cochiti, *Dyámi-hánuch;* Zuñi, *K'yák'yali-kwe;* also a "Painted Eagle" clan, *Sepi^n-tdóa,* at San Juan.

A fine pair of the *Haliæetus leucocephalus leucocephalus* (Linn.) were noted at the Rito de los Frijoles Canyon, August 19, 1910. It is likely that the golden eagle, *Aquila chrysaëtos* (Linn.), occurs also in this region, but we have no definite record of it. The informants said that there is also a kind of eagle which they call *tse· ĩsæ·'i'ⁱ,* 'white eagle' (*tse·,* eagle; *ĩsæ·,* white). This may be the young of the golden eagle. Miss Fletcher speaks of "the white eagle (the young brown or golden eagle)".[1]

Mahuŋ.

Tsiso'jo·, 'big eyes' (*tsi,* eye; *so'jo·,* big). Owl.

Strix occidentalis occidentalis (Xantus). Spotted Owl.

The name *mahuŋ* may be an imitation of the hoot. Cushing gives *"mu'h-hu-tu'"* as a Zuñi imitation of the cry of an owl.[2] The Isleta call owl *hnukuiʌe;* the Jemez, *hunu.*

At least one pair nested at El Rito de los Frijoles, and serenaded our camp nightly. Though we have found no definite record of them, the following species may be expected in the region: Long-eared owl (*Asio wilsonianus* [Lesson]), short-eared owl (*Asio flammeus* [Pont.]), saw-whet owl (*Cryptoglaux acadica acadica* [Gmelin]), Aiken's screech owl (*Otus asio aikeni* [Brewster]), flammulated screech owl (*Otus flammeolus flammeolus* [Kaup]), western horned owl (*Bubo virginianus pallescens* Stone), and Rocky Mountain pygmy owl (*Glaucidium gnoma pinicola* Nelson).

Ki·mahuŋ, 'prairie-dog owl' (*ki·,* prairie-dog; *mahuŋ,* owl).

Speotyto cunicularia hypogæa (Bonaparte). Burrowing Owl.

McCall[3] found it occasionally along the Rio Grande, from Valverde to Santa Fe. It doubtless occurs northward in the valley, especially about prairie-dog colonies.

'Ogowi·.

Geococcyx californianus (Lesson). Road-runner.

The Mexicans of New Mexico call this bird *paisano.* Some Americans have called it chaparral cock.

This long-tailed, long-legged bird seeks safety by running rather than by flying. Judge Abbott says he has seen it occasionally on the mesas within a few miles of the Rito de los Frijoles.

---

[1] A. C. Fletcher, The Hako: A Pawnee Ceremony, *Twenty-second Ann. Rep. Bur. Amer. Ethn.,* pt. 2 p. 21, 1904.

[2] F. H. Cushing, Zuñi Breadstuff, *The Millstone,* x, no. IV, April, 1885, p. 59.

[3] McCall, George A., op. cit., p. 214.

The footprints of the road-runner resemble a letter X. They are called by the same term as the foot itself: *'ogowi·'ą̃ŋ*, 'road-runner foot or footprint' (*'ogowi·*, road-runner; *'ą̃ŋ*, foot, footprint).

Hodge gives as Road-runner clans of various pueblos: Laguna, *Shiáska-háno^ch*; Acoma, *Shásk'-hánoq^ch*; Sia, *Chösh'ka-háno*; San Felipe, *Sösh'ka-háno*; Zuñi, *Póye-kwe*. The Handbook of American Indians (following Fewkes) gives "*Hosboa*" as the Road-runner or Pheasant clan of the Hopi.

P'i'o.

Dryobates villosus monticola Anthony.   Rocky Mountain Hairy Woodpecker(?).[1]

Black above, with white stripe down back, white stripes about head, white spots on wings, white outer tail-feathers, white beneath, and male with red spot on back of head. Common throughout the region— in the canyons, on the mesas, and in the mountains. The alpine three-toed woodpecker (*Picoides americanus dorsalis* Baird) occurs in the high mountains of northern New Mexico.[2] Williamson's sapsucker (*Sphyrapicus thyroideus* [Cassin]) ranges southward as far as central New Mexico and winters in the territory. The northern pileolated woodpecker (*Phlæotomus abieticola* [Bangs]) extends into the forest area of northern New Mexico. If the red-headed woodpecker (*Melanerpes erythrocephalus* [Linn.]) occurs, it is accidental. Lewis's woodpecker (*Asyndesmus lewisi* Riley), black above, reddish beneath, with a gray collar, should occur here.

? ———

Colaptes cafer collaris Vigors.   Red-shafted Flicker.

Very common in the canyons, on the mesas, and in the mountains. Our Indian informants, in describing its habits, told of its boring into trees for "worms" and for nesting sites, but had never observed its very pronounced habit of alighting on the ground and searching for ants, which was a daily sight at the Rito.

? ———

Phalænoptilus nuttalli nuttalli (Aud.).   Poor-will.

We heard the mournful calls of this bird only in the Jemez Mountains, a few miles beyond the headwaters of El Rito de los Frijoles, August 18 and 19, 1910.

? ———.

Chordeiles virginianus henryi Cassin.   Western Nighthawk.

On a cloudy day (August 2) hundreds of these useful birds were circling over the mesa between Santa Fe and Buckman. At the Rito there seemed to be very few of them.

---

[1] The Hairy Woodpecker of Arizona and New Mexico has been described as a new subspecies: *Dryobates villosus leucothorectis* Oberholser. See Oberholser, H. C., A Revision of the Forms of the Hairy Woodpeckers (Dryobates villosus [Linnæus]), *Proc. U. S. Nat. Mus.*, XL, pp. 608–09, 1911.

[2] A. O. U. Check-List of North American Birds, p. 190.

? ——————.

Aëronautes melanoleucus (Baird). White-throated Swift.

Common on the rim of Rio Grande Canyon below the mouth of El Rito de los Frijoles.

Kohe.

Tʻ a ŋkohe, 'sun hummingbird' (*tʻ a ŋ,* sun; *kohe,* hummingbird).

Selasphorus rufus (Gmelin). Rufous Hummingbird.

Very abundant at Rito de los Frijoles Canyon, dozens of them hovering over the patches of "waco," or "bee-plant" (*Cleome serrulata* Pursh.). Specimens taken were identified by Dr. Ridgway. Our Indian informants correctly distinguished the males and females· when shown specimens, noticed that they were found mostly about the *Cleome,* and said they were not found in the Rio Grande Canyon. The broad-tailed hummingbird (*Selasphorus platycercus* [Swainson]), calliope hummingbird (*Stellula calliope* [Gould]), and black-chinned hummingbird (*Archilochus alexandri* [Bourc. & Mul.]) are likely to be found in this region.

Hodge gives *Mi'itsr-hano* as a Hummingbird clan of San Felipe.

Kwæ' æ.

Pica pica hudsonia (Sabine). Magpie.

This conspicuous bird is well known to the Tewa and is mentioned in their mythology.

Tseʻkwæ'æ, 'spruce magpie' (*tseʻ,* Douglas spruce; *kwæ'æ,* magpie).

A kind of magpie.

No particulars could be learned except that this bird is a kind of magpie which frequents *tseʻ* trees.

Seʻ.

Jay.

For the species considered separately, see below.

Hodge gives *Se-tdóa* as a "bluebird" clan of San Ildefonso.

Seʻ.

Cyanocitta stelleri diademata (Bonaparte). Long-crested Jay.

This bird, so easily recognized by its dark blue color and long crest, or topknot, is common all over the region—in the canyons, on the mesas, and in the mountains. Strangely enough, our Indian informants, though quite familiar with the bird, had not noticed that it lowered its crest in flying, but thought the crest was always erect.

Seʻ.

Aphelocoma woodhousei (Baird). Woodhouse's Jay.

This and the piñon jay are readily distinguished from the long-crested jay by the lack of crests. The piñon jay is nearly uniform bluish-gray, the head a trifle darker than the back, lighter blue below, tail shorter than wing; the Woodhouse jay not bluish below, wing shorter than tail. They are both abundant among the piñon pines and cedars of the mesas. We did not observe them in the mountains and seldom in the canyons. The name "piñonero" is applied to both species by the Mexicans, who do not distinguish them apart and find both together among the piñon pines, though Coues and other ornithologists have assumed that it meant only the piñon jay. It is to these two species, probably, that Bandelier refers [1] when he says: "These trees are also beset by flocks of the *Picicorvus columbinus* (called Piñonero in Spanish and sho-hak-ka in Queres), a handsome bird, which ruthlessly plunders the nut-bearing pines, uttering discordant shrieks and piercing cries." These two jays have always been found in large numbers in such situations and could not have escaped his notice, while Clarke's nutcracker, whose former technical name Bandelier used, was not noted by us anywhere in the piñon-cedar belt and would not be so likely to occur there.

Se·.
Perisoreus canadensis capitalis Ridgway.   Rocky Mountain Jay.

This jay, about the size of the preceding species, is very similar to the gray Canada jay or "whisky jack" of the Northeastern States, but its head is almost entirely white. Northern New Mexico is included within its range, but it would likely occur only in the highest mountains except in the winter.

'Oḍo.
Corvus brachyrhynchos brachyrhynchos Brehm.   Crow.

The Tewa appear to designate crow and raven by this one name. Mrs. Stevenson [2] gives "kăka" as the Zuñi word meaning "raven" (or crow?). Cushing [3] tells the Zuñi story of the origin of the crow, in which he says "they (the crows) flew away laughing Kâ-hâ, Kâ-hâ, as they've laughed ever since." The imitated call is interesting in connection with the Zuñi name for crow. In the same article Cushing tells how the Zuñi keep crows away from sprouting corn by means of scarecrows.

As Crow clans at various pueblos Hodge gives: Jemez, *Kyialísh;* Pecos, *Kyiá'hl+;* Sia, *Schíra-háno;* San Felipe, *Schirlá-háno.*

A number of crows were seen and heard in the Jemez Mountains, near Valle Grande, perhaps of this form which is reported on the Pecos, to the eastward, by Mrs. Bailey, though they may be of the western form, *C. b. hesperis* Ridgway. The white-necked raven (*Cor-*

[1] Bandelier, A. F., Final Report, pt. I, *Papers Archæol. Inst. Amer., Amer. Ser.*, IV, p. 150, 1892.
[2] Stevenson, M. C., The Zuñi Indians, *Twenty-third Ann. Rep. Bur. Amer. Ethn.*, p. 51, 1904.
[3] Cushing, F. H., Zuñi Breadstuff, *The Millstone*, May, 1884, pp. 77–78.

vus cryptoleucus Couch) may occur in this region. It was reported at Galisteo, south of Santa Fe, by Goss.[1]

? ———

Nucifraga columbiana (Wilson). Clarke's Nutcracker.

Several were seen in the Jemez Mountains near Valle Grande, and two in Alamo Canyon, about five miles south of El Rito de los Frijoles. They were above the piñon belt. Gray, with black wings and tail, white patch on wing and white outer tail-feathers, this is a striking bird in flight. McCall[2] found it "in the high pine forests east of Santa Fe and on the Taos Mountain."

? ———

Cyanocephalus cyanocephalus (Wied). Piñon Jay.

See discussion of this species under Woodhouse's jay (pp. 39–40). McCall's[3] *Cyanocorax cassinii* is a synonym of this species.

? ———

Xanthocephalus xanthocephalus (Bonaparte). Yellow-headed Blackbird.

Described and reported in the Rio Grande Valley near San Ilde-fonso by our Indian informants, who say they use it for food and that it is seen only in the winter, associated with red-winged black-birds.

? ———

Agelaius phœniceus fortis Ridgway. Thick-billed Red-wing(?).

Reported in the Rio Grande Valley by our San Ildefonso Indian informants, who correctly described the differences between the male and the female, and their nesting sites and habits. They said that the birds are eaten by the Tewa. This subspecies may be *A. p. neutralis* Ridgway.

? ———

Carpodacus cassini Baird. Cassin's Purple Finch.

Reported by Kennerly[4] on "Pueblo Creek" (probably near Taos), January 22, 1854. We have found no subsequent record, though the species probably occurs regularly in the region in the winter. The creek on which Taos pueblo is situated is called Pueblo Creek above its confluence with Arroyo Hondo; the creek north of which Picuris pueblo lies is called Pueblo Creek above its confluence with Peñasco Creek.

? ———

Carpodacus mexicanus frontalis (Say). House Finch.

---

[1] Goss, Nathaniel S., White-Necked Raven (*Corvus cryptoleucus*) in New Mexico, *Bull. Nutt. Orn. Club*, VI, p. 118, 1881.

[2] McCall, George A., op. cit., p. 217.

[3] Ibid., pp. 216–17.

[4] Kennerly, C. B. R., Report on Birds Collected on the Route, Zoological Report, No. 3, p. 27, *Explor. & Surv. for R. R. from Miss. to Pac. Ocean, U. S. War Dept.*, x, 1859.

Common in Santa Fe and probably in all other towns of New Mexico. It is found usually about houses that are surrounded by trees and near an open supply of water. This leads one to wonder whether it did not inhabit El Rito de los Frijoles when the canyon was teeming with human inhabitants. McCall reported it at Santa Fe long ago, and also reported *Carpodacus obscurus* Nobis and described *Carpodacus familiaris* from the same place.[1] These may both be safely referred to *frontalis*.

? ———

Astragalinus psaltria psaltria (Say).   Arkansas Goldfinch.

This tiny bird was abundant especially among the sunflowers—one of the most abundant birds in the canyon of El Rito de los Frijoles.

? ———

Chondestes grammacus strigatus Swainson.   Western Lark Sparrow.

A few were seen by us in the open fields at the foot of the Jemez Mountains, near the old Buckman sawmill. McCall[2] reported it on the plains near Santa Fe.

? *Qwo.è.*

Spizella breweri Cassin.   Brewer's Sparrow.

Very common in the canyon of El Rito de los Frijoles and elsewhere. Reported at Santa Fe by Henshaw.[3]

? ———

Junco phæonotus dorsalis Henry.   Red-backed Junco.

Abundant from base to top of Jemez Mountains, near the head-waters of El Rito de los Frijoles, June 19 and 20, 1910. The gray-headed junco (*Junco phæonotus caniceps* [Woodhouse]) probably also nests in the higher mountains of the region, and several species probably winter there. Our Indian informants recognized pictures and descriptions of juncoes as winter visitors, but were not aware that any species summered in the region.

? ———

Melospiza melodia montana Henshaw.   Mountain Song Sparrow.

Probably it was this species, then undescribed, found by Kennerly[4] at Pueblo Creek, near Taos, and recorded as *M. fallax*.

? ———

Pipilo maculatus montanus Swarth.   Spurred Towhee.

A few were seen in the canyon and on the mesa at El Rito de los Frijoles, but the species is not common. Recorded by Kennerly[5] under

---

[1] McCall, George A., op. cit., pp. 219-20; also Note on Carpodacus frontalis Say, with Description of a New Species of the Same Genus, from Santa Fe, N. Mex., *Proc. Acad. Nat. Sci. Phila.*, VI, p. 61, 1854.

[2] Ibid., p. 218.

[3] Henshaw, H. W., op. cit., p. 280.

[4] Kennerly, C. B. R., op. cit., p. 29.

[5] Ibid., p. 30.

the name *P. megalonyx* at Pueblo Creek. Probably also by McCall,[1]
P. arcticus, at Santa Fe.

? ———

Zamelodia melanocephala (Swainson). Black-headed Grosbeak.
A single pair raised a brood near camp at El Rito de los Frijoles

? ———

Passer domesticus (Linn.). English Sparrow.
Introduced into the territory since 1886. Apt to be found now in
all the more important towns, but probably not in the uninhabited
canyon and mesa regions; certainly unknown to the ancient inhabitants.

? ———

Iridoprocne bicolor (Vieillot). Tree Swallow.
Tachycineta thalassina lepida Mearns. Northern Violet-green
     Swallow.
Several times birds of one or the other of these two species were
seen at El Rito de los Frijoles, but we could seldom get a good view of
them. Our impression is that the latter was represented, and probably
both. The former was reported by McCall[2] as nesting at Santa Fe.

? ———

Dendroica auduboni auduboni (Townsend). Audubon's Warbler.
Common on August 20, 1910, at the foot of the Jemez Mountains,
near the headwaters of El Rito de los Frijoles.

? ———

Geothlypis trichas occidentalis Brewster. Western Yellow-throat.
Our Indian informants describe this species by its color, song, and
habits, as a bird living along the Rio Grande in this region, and when
shown a colored figure of it with pictures of other warblers they at
once recognized it.
Doubtless other species of the wood warbler family pass through
in migration and probably some nest in this region, but no records
are at hand.

Juʼŋ.
Mimus polyglottos leucopterus (Vigors). Western Mockingbird.
Reported near San Ildefonso by one of our Indian informants, who
seemed quite familiar with the bird, knew the white man's name for
it, and described its song as the song of all other birds combined.
The whites report it at Santa Fe.

? ———

Salpinctes obsoletus obsoletus [Say]. Rock Wren.

---

[1] McCall, George A., op. cit., p. 218.   [2] Ibid., p. 215.

One taken by us on the rim of the Rio Grande Canyon below the mouth of El Rito de los Frijoles. Reported abundant at Santa Fe by Henshaw.[1]

? ———

Catherpes mexicanus conspersus Ridgway. Canyon Wren.

Common along all the canyon cliffs of this region. The song of the male, usually of about seven loud, ringing notes descending the scale, makes it the most noticeable of the wrens.

? ———

Troglodytes aëdon parkmani Audubon. Western House Wren.

Common in the canyons and on the mesas.

? ———

Sitta carolinensis nelsoni Mearns. Rocky Mountain Nuthatch.

Common on the mesas and in the mountains. We saw none in the canyons cutting the mesas.

? ———

Sitta pygmæa pygmæa Vigors. Pygmy Nuthatch.

Abundant in the canyons, on the mesas, and in the mountains. This tiny species was everywhere to be found in numbers among the pines.

? ———

Bæolophus inornatus griseus (Ridgway). Gray Titmouse.

Very common among the piñon pines and cedars on the mesas.

? ———

Penthestes gambeli gambeli (Ridgway). Mountain Chickadee.

Very abundant in the canyons, on the mesas, and in the mountains. The type locality for this species is "about one day's journey west of Santa Fe," which would be not far from El Rito de los Frijoles. We saw no long-tailed chickadees (*Penthestes atricapillus septentrionalis* [Harris]).

? ———

Myadestes townsendi (Aud.). Townsend's Solitaire.

Common in the canyon at Painted Cave, 5 miles or more south of El Rito de los Frijoles.

? ———

Hylocichla fuscescens salicicola Ridgway. Willow Thrush.

A pair raised a brood at El Rito de los Frijoles in 1910. Recorded also from Pueblo Creek, near Taos Pueblo, in 1904, by Mrs. Bailey.[2]

? ———.

Planesticus migratorius propinquus (Ridgway). Western Robin.

Common in the canyons and in the mountains.

[1] Henshaw, H. W., op. cit., p. 180.   [2] Bailey, Florence Merriam, op. cit., pp. 317–18.

ʔ ——ˑ.

Sialia mexicana bairdi Ridgway. Chestnut-backed Bluebird.

Abundant everywhere on the mesas, but none in the canyons. Our Indian informants had noted the same fact.

Palomà (<Span. *paloma*).

Domestic Pigeon.

Gatschet [1] incorrectly gives "paróma" as the Tesuque name for pigeon.

Perikù (<Span. *perico*).

Palì (<Eng. polly).

Hodge gives as a Parrot clan of Zuñi, distinct from the Macaw clan, *Píohi-kwe*; there is also the testimony of Lummis that there is no Parrot clan at Isleta.

Tañį̀.

Macaw.

This is the bird which the Mexicans call *guacamayo*. Its feathers are highly prized by the Tewa for ceremonial purposes. They state that the feathers and also live *tañį̀* were obtained from Mexico in former times. The informants stated that a *tañį̀* is at the present time kept in a cage at Santo Domingo pueblo.

Hodge gives as Parrot clans of various pueblos (which are possibly Macaw clans): Laguna, *Sháwïtï-háno^{ch}*; Acoma, *Sháwït^i-hanoq^{ch}*; Sia and Santa Ana, *Shô'wïti-háno*; San Felipe, *Shô'wati-háno*; and as a Macaw clan of Zuñi, *Múlakwe*.

Tsiʌe ȋse·jì'^i, 'yellow bird' (*tsiʌe*, bird; *ȋse·*, yellow).

Canary.

Some of the Mexicans who live in the Tewa country keep these birds in cages and call them *canarios*.

Paɓoʌeal (<Span. *pavo real*).

Peacock.

Some of the Mexicans who live in the Tewa country keep these birds.

The following are Tewa names of birds which we have not yet been able to identify with scientific names:

Petsep‛e'e'e·, perhaps the oriole.

K̄aʌaŋwǽ·, said to be similar to *ñǽ·qwoʌè*.

Ñǽ·qwoʌè, said to be similar to *k̄aʌaŋwǽ·*.

Kwą́·qweʌè, perhaps the common house swallow.

Po·sak̄ǽ·, described as a small bird with needle-like nose.

Ɲwǽ·ŋtsiʌe, 'pine bird' (*ɲwǽ·ŋ*, Pinus scopulorum; *tsiʌe*, bird).
    This is described as a small bird with gray body and white
    head, which jumps about in the rock-pines.

---

[1] A. S. Gatschet, Zwölf Sprachen aus dem Südwesten Nordamerikas, Weimer, 1876, p. 40.

Tsiʌe p̂i'i'i, 'red bird' (*tsiʌe*, bird; *p̂i*·, red), applies to one or more species of small red bird.

Kųsę·ŋ, a small bird.

'Oñų'e·, perhaps a species of blackbird.

'Ogoja·.

Ka·wo·.

Piju.

K'u·tsiʌe.

Tse·ką̆ną̆ tsiʌe.

Ka·tsiʌe, 'leaf bird' (*ka*·, leaf; *tsiʌe*, bird), a kind of small yellow bird.

Te·tse· (of obscure etymology), a species of small yellowish bird seen in cottonwood and other trees.

P̂o·jų·ŋ, 'water mockingbird' (*p̂o*·, water; *jų·ŋ*, mockingbird), a small, inconspicuous bird seen by water. Possibly the dipper (water ouzel), *Cinclus mexicanus unicolor* Bonaparte.

P̂o·te'ji, probably the killdeer or "tildee." The first syllable sounds like *p̂o*·, 'water.'

P̂o·k̂epę·ŋ, 'water bent neck' (*p̂o*·, water; *k̂e*, neck; *pę·ŋ*, bent), some kind of water bird. It has long legs and is seen along the Rio Grande. Probably a heron.

Kwą̆·pijè, 'toward rain' (*kwą̆*·, rain; *pijè*, toward), a heron-like species of bird.

K'â'æwi. A kind of blue bird seen in piñon trees. It is thought by the informant that Mexicans call it piñonero.

Tsą̆'æ'ᵆ. A large kind of bird.

T̂į·ŋ'e·. A species of large red bird.

Puga. This is the bird which the Mexicans call *grulla*. It is a large, buff-colored bird seen wading or walking by the river. When it migrates it flies in a V-shape, making at times a peculiar whirring or trilled noise which can be heard even though the birds be high in the air. Mrs. Stevenson[1] mentions the sandhill crane as known at Zuñi.

Hodge gives as Crane or Heron clans of various pueblos: Hano, *Kapúlo-tówa* (the Rio Grande Tewa do not know the word *kapúlo*); Sia, *Shúta-hano;* Zuñi, *Kâ'lokta-kwe*.

Reptiles

The smaller lizards, especially the swifts, are very abundant throughout the region. Horned lizards (popularly called "horned toads") are by no means infrequent. The larger lizards are either not abundant or more adept at escaping observation. None of the lizards found here are poisonous. The only known poisonous lizards

[1] Stevenson, M. C., The Zuñi Indians, *Twenty-third Ann. Rep. Bur. Amer. Ethn.*, p. 292, 1904.

of the New World appear to be the Gila monster and the Mexican beaded lizard, neither of which occurs in northern New Mexico. Among the snakes the only poisonous one known in the region is the rattlesnake. The wound made by any reptile or other animal having teeth capable of lacerating the epidermis or flesh may of course become infected, just as a scratch produced by any inorganic substance may, and thus create the impression that the poison was injected at the time of the bite. Our Indian informants considered the swifts and horned lizards harmless, but declared that the Sonora skink, of which a specimen was found by them, is poisonous. The Indians have the same so-called instinctive dread for the larger reptiles, particularly snakes, as the whites, being startled when suddenly they come upon one, and disliking to handle them. They informed us that neither snakes nor lizards are used as food at present by the Tewa, but it is not unlikely that their ancestors used them, at least during times of famine. However, they could not have been at any time more than an insignificant article of food.

There appears to be a widespread belief that the Indians of the Southwest generally are addicted to the use of reptiles for food. Whatever may be true of the past, this is not the case now. Russell's statement concerning the Pima Indians,[1] that "snakes are not eaten, even in times of famine, and the idea of eating lizards is repudiated with scorn," is applicable to many other Southwestern tribes.

LIZARDS

? ———.

Crotaphytus collaris baileyi (Stejneger). Bailey's Collared Lizard. This fine lizard probably occurs throughout the region, though we saw none. *C. collaris* was reported at Santa Fe and San Ildefonso by Yarrow and Cope [2] long before the subspecies *baileyi* was described, but Stejneger [3] places our area within the range of *baileyi* and represents *collaris* as occurring from Pecos Valley eastward.

? ———

Holbrookia maculata maculata (Girard). Common Spotted Lizard.

---

[1] Russell, Frank, The Pima Indians, *Twenty-sixth Ann. Rep. Bur. Amer. Ethn.*, p. 83, 1908.

[2] Yarrow, H. C., Report upon the Collections of Batrachians and Reptiles made in Portions of Nevada, Utah, California, Colorado, New Mexico and Arizona during the years 1871, 1872, 1873 and 1874, *U. S. Geog. Explor. and Survey W. of 100th Meridian*, v, p. 566, 1875; Check-List of North American Reptilia and Batrachia, with Catalogue of Specimens in U. S. National Museum, *Bull. U. S. Nat. Museum, no. 24*, p. 52, 1882. Cope, E. D., The Crocodilians, Lizards, and Snakes of North America, *Ann. Rep. U. S. Nat. Museum for 1898*, pp. 248–53, 1900.

[3] Stejneger, Leonhard, Annotated List of Reptiles and Batrachians Collected by Dr. C. Hart Merriam and Vernon Bailey on the San Francisco Mountain Plateau and Desert of the Little Colorado, Arizona, with descriptions of New Species, *North American Fauna*, no. 3, U. S. Dept. Agr., pp. 103–05, pl. XIII, 1890. Ruthven, A. G., A Collection of Reptiles and Amphibians from Southern New Mexico and Arizona, *Bull. Amer. Mus. Nat. Hist.*, XXIII, pp. 512–14, 1907.

Reported at Santa Fe, Abiquiu, San Ildefonso, and Plaza del Alcalde by Yarrow and Cope.[1]

? ———

Uta stansburiana Baird & Girard.   Stansbury's Small-scaled Swift.

Reported at San Ildefonso by Yarrow and Cope.[2]

? ———

Uta levis Stejneger.   Olive Small-scaled Swift.

Type locality is Tierra Amarilla.[3]   This appears to be Yarrow's record[4] under the name *Uta ornata* Baird & Girard.   Our Indian informants say that snakes swallow these lizards.   They are harmless.

? ———

Sceloporus undulatus consobrinus (Baird & Girard).   Yellow-banded Spiny-scaled Swift.

Yarrow reported this species from Santa Fe and described *Sceloporus tristichus* from Taos, the description being written by Cope apparently.   Afterward Yarrow reported *tristichus* from Taos and *consobrinus* from both Taos and Santa Fe.   Cope later repeated Yarrow's records for both localities, but made both of them subspecies of *undulatus*.[5]   Ditmars[6] ignores *tristichus*.   Small lizards of this group are very abundant at El Rito de los Frijoles, darting in and out among the rocks and logs everywhere in the canyon.   The only specimens we collected are assigned to *consobrinus*.

Koʌohį̓y.

Phrynosoma douglassii hernandesi (Girard).   Western Horned Lizard.

Reported at Taos, Santa Fe, Abiquiu, and San Ildefonso by Yarrow and Cope.[7]   We collected two specimens of horned lizard at El Rito de los Frijoles, and both are *hernandesi*.   Our Indian informants declared that snakes swallow these lizards, swell up, burst, and the lizard comes out alive.   This is not more fantastic than some of the popular notions of white people concerning animals.   The name "horned toad," usually applied to this animal, should be dropped even from popular literature, as it belongs distinctly to the Reptilia and not to the Amphibia.

Koʌohį̓y.

Phrynosoma douglassii ornatissimum (Girard).   Ornate Horned Lizard.

[1] Yarrow, H. C., Report, op. cit., p. 569; Check-List, op. cit., pp. 56–57.   Cope, E. D., op. cit., pp. 293–97.
[2] Yarrow, H. C., Report, op. cit., p. 566; Check-List, op. cit., p. 49.   Cope, op. cit., p. 310.
[3] Stejneger, op. cit., p. 108.   Cope, op. cit., p. 313.
[4] Yarrow, H. C., Check-List, op. cit., p. 56.
[5] Yarrow, H. C., Report, op. cit., p. 572; Check-List, op. cit., pp. 61–62.   Cope, E. D., op. cit., pp. 376–81.
[6] Ditmars, R. L., Reptile Book, New York, 1907.
[7] Yarrow, H. C., Report, op. cit., p. 581; Check-List, op. cit., pp. 68–69.   Cope, E. D., op. cit., pp. 413–15.

Reported at Santa Fe by Yarrow and Cope.[1]

Koɹohįɲ.

Phrynosoma cornutum Harlan.   Southern Horned Lizard.

Reported at San Ildefonso and Abiquiu by Yarrow,[2] and at Taos, Abiquiu, and San Ildefonso by Cope.[3]

Koɹohįɲ.

Anota modesta Girard.   Little Horned Lizard.

Recorded at San Ildefonso by Yarrow and Cope.[4]

? ———

Cnemidophorus tessellatus perplexus (Baird & Girard).   Seven-
striped Lizard.

Recorded at San Ildefonso by Yarrow and Cope.[5]   This is Yarrow's *C. octolineatus* Baird, from the same locality.[6]   Possibly the sub-specific name *perplexus* should be dropped.

? ———

Cnemidophorus sexlineatus (Linn.).   Six-lined Lizard.

Recorded at Santa Fe, Plaza del Alcalde, and Abiquiu to Jemez, by Yarrow and Cope.[7]   This record possibly should be referred to *C. gularis* Baird & Girard.

Ḳod̨u'u.

Eumeces obsoletus (Baird & Girard).   Sonora Skink.

Two fine specimens of this lizard, with the edges of the scales quite dark, were unearthed by the Indians in excavating the old pueblo at El Rito de los Frijoles.   One was captured, the other escaped.   Old men of San Ildefonso declared that it is poisonous and would not touch it.   They have a "remedy" for its bite.   They are mistaken as to its poisonous character.   The Mexicans call this kind of lizard *escurpion*.

Besides the *koɹohįɲ*, 'horned lizard,' which the Mexicans call *camaleon*, the Tewa have names for five other kinds of native lizards:

Qwi·pa·je is a lizard which is sometimes as long as the *tsæ·qwijè* (see below).   It is blue-bellied and gray-backed.

Tsǫ·ɲdę̀, a lizard of bluish color, a little longer than the *tse·ɹàqwįɲ*.

Tse·ɹàqwįɲ, a species of small, inconspicuous lizard.   The description reminds one of the swift.   The first syllable of the name seems to be *tse·*, 'face.'

Tsæ·qwijè, 'white stripes' (*tsæ·*, white; *qwijè*, stripe).   This lizard has white stripes down its back.

1 Yarrow, H. C , Check-List, op. cit., p. 69.   Cope, E. D., op. cit., p. 417.
2 Yarrow, H. C., Report, op. cit., p. 579; Check-List, op. cit., p. 66.
3 Cope, E. D., op. cit., p. 436.
4 Yarrow, H. C., Check-List, op. cit., p. 64.   Cope, E. D., op. cit., p. 439.
5 Yarrow, Check-List, op. cit., p. 44.   Cope, E. D., op. cit., p. 574.
6 Yarrow, H. C., Report, op. cit., p. 558.
7 Yarrow, H. C., Report, op. cit., p. 558; Check-List, op. cit., p. 43.   Cope, E. D., op. cit., p. 597.

Kajimạŋ (<Span. *calliman*).

Alligator.

One of these animals was exhibited in a pool-room at Santa Fe.

SNAKES

? ———

Heterodon nasicus nasicus (Baird & Girard).   Western Hog-nosed Snake.

Recorded at Santa Clara, San Ildefonso, and Abiquiu by Yarrow,[1] and at Santa Fe by Cope.[2]

? ———

Zamenis constrictor flaviventris (Say).   Blue Racer, Green Racer.

Recorded from Tierra Amarilla by Yarrow under the name *Z. c. vetustum* in his report, and under the name *flaviventris* in his Check-List.   Cope records a young specimen which is probably the same.[3] Several snakes were seen at El Rito de los Frijoles early in August, 1910, which were probably this species, but they escaped and none was seen afterward except a young specimen taken August 25, beautifully marked, very much like the bull snake, quite unlike the adult.   A San Ildefonso Indian informant called this young specimen *ną́·ypæñụ*.   (See p. 51.)   Having no adult specimens we could not learn whether they would recognize the young and adult as the same kind or designate them by the same name, though the latter is highly improbable.

? ———

Pityophis catenifer sayi (Schlegel).   Bull Snake.

It is probably this species which was recorded as *P. sayi mexicanus* Dum. & Bib., by Yarrow, at San Ildefonso.[4]   A bull snake was described to us at El Rito de los Frijoles by Judge Abbott in August, 1910, but he did not capture it for identification.

? ———

Thamnophis eques (Reuss).   Brown Garter Snake.

Cope recorded *Eutænia eques aurata* Cope from San Ildefonso, and *E. sirtalis dorsalis* Baird & Girard from the same place.   Yarrow recorded *Eutænia ornata* Baird at Abiquiu and San Ildefonso.   These, it appears, should all be referred to *T. eques*, which is recorded from San Ildefonso by Ruthven.[5]

---

[1] Yarrow, H. C., Report, op. cit., p. 556; Check-List, op. cit., p. 141.

[2] Cope, E. D., op. cit., p. 777.

[3] Yarrow, H. C., Report, op. cit., p. 542; Check-List, op. cit., p. 110. Cope, E. D., op. cit., p. 797.

[4] Yarrow, H. C., Report, op. cit., p. 540. See Ruthven, A. G., in *Bull. Amer. Mus. Nat. Hist.*, XXIII. pp. 581–86, 1907.

[5] Yarrow, H. C., Report, op. cit., p. 554; Check-List, op. cit, p. 122. Cope, E. D., op. cit., p. 1077. Ruthven, A. G., Variations and Genetic Relationships of the Garter-Snakes, *Bull. 61, U. S. Nat. Mus.*, pp. 158–60, 1908.

Qwǽ·ŋpу·, 'tail rattle' (*qwǽ·ŋ*, tail; *pу·*, rattle).   Rattlesnakes of
any species and also their rattles are called *qwǽ·ŋpу·*.   (See
below.)

Crotalus sp.   Rattlesnake.

Several species of rattlesnake have been recorded from New Mexico,
but none from the area under discussion, so far as we are aware.   Two
specimens have been killed at El Rito de los Frijoles within two or
three years, as we are informed by Judge Abbott and Mr. Dowell,
but they were not specifically identified.   The Indians say rattlesnakes are common in the Rio Grande Canyon not far from the Rito.
C. confluentus confluentus (Say) probably occurs in this region, and
perhaps other species.

Any species of snake is called *pǽñу*.   The following kinds are
known by name:

Pi·su, 'red arrow' (*pi·*, red; *su*, arrow).   These slender red snakes
almost fly through the air, according to the natives.

Tsiуpǽñу, 'basalt snake' (*tsi*, basalt rock; *pǽñу*, snake).

Nǫ̀·ŋpǽñу, 'earth snake' (*nǫ̀·ŋ*, earth; *pǽñу*, snake).   These are
brownish.

Po·pǽñу, 'water snake' (*po·*, water; *pǽñу*, snake).   Any kind of
water snake may be called thus.

Po·mǫ·qwi·ḅeg'è (*po·*, water; *mǫ·*, (?); *qwi·*tied, tangled, a knot, a
thicket; *ḅeg'è*, low place, dell, low corner).   What the name means is
not clear.   This is a kind of water snake, possibly a synonym of
po·pǽñу.

'*Usiḍi*, a snake a yard long, "earth-colored."

Nǫ̀·'ǫ·, San Ildefonso dialect *nǫ̀·ŋḍa·*.   A kind of snake longer than
nǫ̀·ŋpǽñу.

Pǽñу p'ę·ŋdi'ⁱ, 'black snake' (*pǽñу*, snake; *p'ę·ŋ*, black).   A dark-
colored snake species.

Qwǽ·ŋpу·, 'tail bell' (*qwǽ·ŋ*, tail; *pу·*, bell or rattle).   This name
applies to any kind of rattlesnake, and is given above.   *Pу·* now
usually means bell of any kind; formerly it referred to anything
which gave out a note when struck or made a rattling sound.   Ex-
amine: *nǽ·i'ⁱ pǽñу nǫ̀qwǽ·ŋpу·mу· qwǽ·ŋdiwe*, 'this snake has a rattle
on its tail' (*nǽ·*, this; *pǽñу*, snake; *nǫ̀*, it; *qwǽ·ŋ*, tail; *pу·*, bell;
mу·, to be, to be provided with; *qwǽ·ŋ*, tail; '*iwe*, locative); *tǽ'ᵉ
'уfsi·gìmу·*, it has ten rattles' (*tǽ'ᵉ*, ten; '*у*, it, with reference to it;
fsi·gì, notch, narrow place; *mу·*, to be, to be provided with).

Of snakes one says either *nǫ̀mǽ·*, 'it goes' (*nǫ̀*, it; *mǽ·*, to go), or
'*iqwa·mǽ·ŋ*, 'it crawls' ('*i*, it; *qwa·mǽ·ŋ*, to go crawlingly, like a man
on all fours).

TURTLES

Only one name for species of turtle or tortoise was obtained from the Tewa—this is *'o·ku·*.

The *'o·ku·* is common in the region. These turtles are found mostly in meadows. They are killed and the carapaces are cleaned and worn by dancers.

AMPHIBIANS (BATRACHIANS)

The amphibians of the region are not very important. Salamanders are rare, and the lack of water restricts frogs and toads to limited areas. Except the frogs, they are of no food value. None of them is poisonous, though it seems that the whites generally look upon the spotted salamander with fear. Having no specimens we could not determine whether the Indians had the same dread.

?————

Ambystoma tigrinum (Green).   Tiger Salamander.

Reported at Santa Fe Creek, under the name *Ambystoma mavortium* Baird, by Yarrow,[1] and by Cope[2] under the name *tigrinum*. *Ambystoma trisruptum* Cope was credited to Santa Fe by Yarrow,[3] but Cope[4] says the only known specimen is from Ocate Creek, east of the mountains in northern New Mexico, and hence not in the Rio Grande drainage.

?————

Spelerpes multiplicatus Cope(?).

We found a small salamander rather common under aspen logs near Valle Grande, in the Jemez Mountains. Specimens badly injured in transit were doubtfully identified as this species by Dr. Leonhard Stejneger. The Indians to whom it was shown were not familiar with it and had no name for it.

?————

Bufo lentiginosus woodhousei (Girard).   Rocky Mountain Toad.

Bufo lentiginosus woodhousei was reported at Santa Fe and Plaza del Alcalde in 1874, by Yarrow,[5] who remarked that it was "apparently numerous in New Mexico." In his Check-List[6] he gives the Plaza del Alcalde record under the name *americanus*, does not recognize *woodhousei* as a distinct form, and omits the Santa Fe record.

[1] Yarrow, H. C., Check-List of North American Reptilia and Batrachia, with Catalogue of Specimens in U. S. National Museum, *Bull. 24, U. S. Nat. Museum*, p. 149, 1882.

[2] Cope, E. D., The Batrachia of North America, *Bull. 34, U. S. Nat. Museum*, p. 85, 1889.

[3] Yarrow, H. C., op. cit., p. 150.

[4] Cope, op. cit., p. 86.

[5] Yarrow, H. C., Report upon the Collections of Batrachians and Reptiles Made in Portions of Nevada, Utah, California, Colorado, New Mexico, and Arizona, During the Years 1871, 1872, 1873, and 1874, *U. S. Geog. Explor. & Surv. W. of 100th Merid.*, v, p. 521, 1875.

[6] Yarrow, H. C., Check-List, etc., op. cit., p. 166.

Cope [1] recognizes *woodhousei* and records it from other localities in New Mexico, but not from these two places or from anywhere in our area, and preserves Yarrow's *americanus* record at Plaza del Alcalde. Miss Dickerson [2] raises *americanus* to a full species, and says it "is the common toad east of the Rocky Mountains from Mexico to the Great Bear Lake," while she leaves *woodhousei* as a subspecies of *lentiginosus* and says it is "the common toad of the Rocky Mountain region," having been reported from a number of States, including New Mexico. Ruthven [3] says it is the "common toad of the Great Plains and Great Basin region."

Our San Ildefonso Indian informants reported "two kinds of frogs" in the region of the Rito de los Frijoles, one of which is found in the water, the other being larger and flatter and is found "jumping" about on land. Probably the latter is a toad. As *Bufo cognatus* Say is reported from Colorado, Kansas, and Arizona, it may extend across New Mexico, or at least be found in the northern portion.

? ———

Rana pipiens Schreber. Leopard Frog.

Frogs were recorded at Taos, Abiquiu, and Santa Fe under the name *Rana halecina berlandieri* (Kalm) Cope, and at Taos under the name *Rana halecina halecina* (Kalm) Cope, by Yarrow.[4] Cope afterward transferred these records to *Rana virescens brachycephala* Cope.[5] Miss Dickerson [6] says *virescens* is Schreber's *pipiens*, which she is unable to separate into subspecies. Further study of this variable frog, based on large quantities of fresh material from widely separated and numerous localities, is desirable. We saw several frogs at El Rito de los Frijoles, but unfortunately obtained none. (See note on Rocky Mountain toad, page 52.)

SALAMANDERS, FROGS, TOADS

The Tewa appear to have but one name for all species of salamanders, and but one name for all species of frogs and toads.

Poʻqwæ· means salamander. The first syllable is clearly the word meaning 'water.'

Pʻęŋkwą̨ŋ is applied to frogs and toads. Tadpoles are called *pʻęŋkukeʌe* in the San Juan dialect, and either *poʻsakeʌe* or *pʻęŋpu-keʌe* in the San Ildefonso dialect. The etymology of these words is not clear. It was thought by one informant that the tadpole's tail drops off.

---

[1] Cope, E. D., op. cit., pp. 281–88.
[2] Dickerson, Mary C., The Frog Book, pp. 63, 91–92, New York, 1906.
[3] Ruthven, A. G., A Collection of Reptiles and Amphibians from Southern New Mexico and Arizona, *Bull. Amer. Mus. Nat. Hist*, XXIII, p. 509, 1907.
[4] Yarrow, H. C., Check-List, op. cit., p. 181.
[5] Cope, E. D., op. cit., pp. 403–04.
[6] Dickerson, Mary C., op. cit., p. 171.

FISHES

Most of the lateral canyons of the region are dry or nearly dry through most of the year, and hence contain no fishes. The Rio Grande is known to contain fishes in some portions of its course.

The Rito de los Frijoles is at present a small stream, the waters of which in places sink entirely beneath the surface of the sand, leaving not even pools, and the water all along becomes very shallow at times. Limited observations make final conclusions unsafe, but so far as they go they seem to indicate that the water flowing in the creek is dependent largely on precipitation in the mountains at the head of the canyon. When frequent rains were occurring in the lower part of the valley the stream reached its lowest point, but during an exceedingly dry period at our camp, when it was raining daily in the mountains the stream kept an even flow. The absence of deep pools in which fish could survive an extended drouth seems sufficient to account for their absence. In the glaciated mountains farther north, the absence of fish is usually noted in streams whose courses present cataracts too high for the fishes to pass over in their upstream progression after the retreat of the glaciers. Two vertical falls near the mouth of this canyon, one of 60 feet, the other of 90 feet, would effectually block the attempts of fish to pass upstream from the Rio Grande. Hence any fish which may have existed in recent times must have been there before the falls were formed or have been introduced in some unusual way. The transportation of eggs attached to the feet of birds for the short distance over the falls would not be at all impossible, though such a method of dispersion is not so likely to occur as in case of fresh-water mollusks, etc. It is also possible that fish may at one time have been placed in this creek by former inhabitants, either the ancient dwellers who built the abandoned structures or by the Mexican outlaws who made the canyon their rendezvous for a century or so. At any rate, trout were found in the stream from 20 to 30 years ago, according to information gleaned from several sources. Bandelier, in *The Delight Makers*, causes one of the native boys who lived in the canyon during its early occupancy, to catch a trout. This would scarcely be conclusive if it were not that in his formal report he refers to the stream as a "gushing brook, enlivened by trout." [1] Dr. Charles F. Lummis, of Los Angeles, says he caught trout from the stream in 1891, and that there were certainly many pools then which do not exist now. Judge Abbott says he has heard the same from another visitor to the canyon a quarter of a century ago.

[1] Bandelier, A. F., The Delight Makers, New York, 1890, p. 5. Final Report of Investigations Among the Indians of the Southwestern United States, Carried on Mainly in the Years from 1880 to 1885, Part II, *Papers of the Archæological Institute of America, American Series*, IV, p. 139, 1892.

The present absence of trout has been locally attributed to a heavy flood which is said to have washed them away. There is evidence along the bottom-lands that such a flood did occur, but that it washed the trout out is highly improbable. It seems much more probable that it may have filled the pools that once made it possible for trout to survive protracted dry seasons, though it is not impossible that the filling is due to the fact that the desiccation of the country has at last reached a point where the stream is not able to take care of the débris arising from lateral erosion of the valley. It is not at all improbable that the creek may have completely dried up during some particularly dry cycle within the last 20 years. In any event we must believe that there were trout a quarter of a century ago, and so we have no reason to doubt that they existed during the occupancy of the valley by the ancient inhabitants, though that is not a necessary conclusion. Of course we have no definite evidence as to the species, but it was almost certainly the Rio Grande Basin trout (*Salmo mykiss spilurus* Cope).

Cope[1] says he saw *Gila pandora* Cope (= *Richardsonius pulchellus pandora* Cope—Cockerell) in the creek below Ojo Caliente. Cope and Yarrow[2] reported the following species from nearby Rio Grande drainage localities, to which species we have applied probable modern nomenclature, placing in parentheses the names under which they were reported:

Pantosteus plebeius Baird & Girard (*P. jarrovii* Cope). Sucker. Taos, San Ildefonso, and Tierra Amarilla.

Hybognathus nuchalis Agassiz. Silvery Minnow. San Ildefonso.

Richardsonius pulchellus pandora (Cope) (*Gila pandora*). Northern Rio Grande Dace. Near San Ildefonso.

Notropis simus Cope (*Alburnellus simus*). Rio Grande Shiner. San Ildefonso.

Notropis dilectus Girard (*Alburnellus jemezanus* Cope). San Ildefonso.

Notropis lutrensis Baird and Girard (*Hypsilepis iris* Cope). San Ildefonso.

---

[1] Cope, E. D., Report upon the Extinct Vertebrata Obtained in New Mexico by Parties of the Expedition of 1874, *Geog. Surv. W. of 100th Merid.* (Wheeler Survey), IV, pt. II, p. 21. See also *Ann. Rept. for 1875*, p. 66, 1875.

[2] Cope, E. D., and Yarrow, H. C., Report upon the Collections of Fishes Made in Portions of Nevada, Utah, California, Colorado, New Mexico, and Arizona, During the Years 1871, 1872, 1873, and 1874, *Geog. Surv. W. of 100th Merid.* (Wheeler Survey), V, pp. 635–703, 1875. See also Cockerell, T. D. A., The Nomenclature of the American Fishes Usually Called Leuciscus and Rutilus, *Proc. Biol. Soc. Wash.*, XXII, pp. 215–17, 1909; The Fishes of the Rocky Mountain Region, *Univ. Colo. Studies*, V, pp. 159–178, 1908; Jordan, David Starr, and Evermann, Barton Warren, The Fishes of North and Middle America, *Bull. 47, U. S. Nat. Mus.*, 4 vols., 1896–1900.

69231°—Bull. 56—14——5

Rhinichthys cataractæ dulcis Girard (*R. maxillosus* Cope). Sweet-water Dace. Tierra Amarilla, Abiquiu, San Ildefonso, and Taos.

Hybopsis æstivalis (Girard) (*Ceratichthys sterletus* Cope). Horny-head. San Ildefonso.

Anguilla rostrata (Le Sueur) (*A. tyrannus* Girard). Fresh-water Eel. Near Santa Fe.

They also report *Salmo pleuriticus* Cope from Rio Taos, Chama River, and near San Ildefonso, but as this species seems to be confined to the Colorado River basin the record is probably a mistake. There are perhaps other fishes existing in the Rio Grande drainage of northern New Mexico, but we have found no record of them. The species are mostly small and of little food value. There are rumors of catfish, but no definite record.

The Tewa have the following names for species of fish:

P̂įŋpa·, 'mountain fish' (*p̂į·ŋ*, mountain; *pa·*, fish). This name seems to be applied to any species of trout.

Pa·tsi·jo·, 'knife fish' (*pa·*, fish; *tsi·jo·*, knife). This fish lives in the Rio Grande. It has a knife-like back, and there is also a knife-like projection at each side of its lower jaw. It reaches a length exceeding a foot.

Pa·wa·p'a·, 'flat-chested fish' (*pa·*, fish; *wa·*, chest, breast; *p'a·*, flat and roundish). This fish lives in the Rio Grande and attains a length of 2 feet or more. Its underside is flat.

Tsewìgè. This fish lives in the Rio Grande. White men in talking to our informants had called this fish a "sucker."

Pa·tųŋwæ·, 'tall fish' (*pa·*, fish; *tųŋwæ·*, tall). This fish lives in the Rio Grande. The Mexicans call it *boquinete*.

Pa·'e·, 'little fish' (*pa·*, fish; *'e·*, diminutive). This term is applied to any small fish, especially to minnows and the like; also to the young of larger varieties of fish, which often can not be recognized as they can when more mature.

Pa·'oqwi·, 'phlegm fish' (*pa·*, fish; *'oqwi·*, mucus from the trachea, bronchial tubes, or lungs, such as is coughed up). This name is applied to any species of eel. The skin of the *pa·'oqwi·* is highly prized and is used among other purposes for leggings and moccasins. The fish lives in the Rio Grande.

It is said that the kinds of fish which live in the Rio Grande would probably also be found in the Rio Chama.

INSECTS

Notwithstanding their average small size, when compared with vertebrates, insects are very important from the point of view of natural history. Their interesting habits, their economic relations to other animals, and the exceedingly large number of known species give them zoological prominence. Their relations to the pollenization of plants and their destructiveness to vegetation give them both botanical and economic importance. Their relation to the spread of disease and the annoying habits of some of them have a direct bearing on the comfort and happiness of the human race.

From the ethnological point of view the position of insects is a minor one. They have little importance as food, except the grasshoppers, etc., during seasons of abundance. Among native peoples of the lower Colorado Valley insects have acquired considerable religious and mythical significance, especially the ants, but this does not require a knowledge of many species or a very minute discrimination between species. Among the Pueblos they have no such significance. A great number of insect species have been recorded from the Jemez Plateau and Santa Fe. There are doubtless hundreds of others unrecorded, including many now undescribed and unknown to science. As most of the smaller species are distinguished from one another by characters which may be studied only with a good lens or a microscope, it is obvious that in most cases the Indians can not distinguish the species or even the genera. However, the larger and more conspicuously marked species are likely given definite native names. It would be an interesting contribution to the psychology of the Indians for someone with sufficient entomological training to investigate their knowledge of and ideas concerning the insects and the extent and accuracy of their discrimination, including the habits of insects and their relations to plants.

Time did not permit us to enter into this field except in an incidental way in connection with the ethnobotanical work. Our collections of insects were accidentally almost wholly destroyed in transit, without having been determined or recorded, so that we can not even give an account of the species found. We found many species of beetles, ants, bees, wasps, butterflies, moths, flies, and other insects.

It does not seem important in this report to list the species of insects recorded from the region by Ashmead, Banks, Cockerell, Coquillett, Dunning, Fall, Fox, Gillette, Hagen, Holland, Howard, Hulst, Mead, Scudder, Thomas, Townsend, Uhler, Ulke, and Wheeler. More than 30 of Prof. Cockerell's papers report species from this region. Ulke has recorded 56 species of Coleoptera (beetles), and Uhler has recorded 34 species of Hemiptera (plant-lice, scale insects, true bugs, etc.) from San Ildefonso, Taos, Santa Fe, Abiquiu, and Tierra Amarilla. Hagen recorded three species of Neuroptera from San Ildefonso, Tierra Amarilla, and Taos. Most of the other records are from Santa Fe.

Work along this line could be easily done by persons with very limited knowledge of entomology. They could collect the insects and preserve them, number the labels, obtain the ethnological data, preserving the connections by referring to the label numbers, and the specimens could then be determined accurately by specialists.

That many of the western Indians did not formerly disdain insects as a part of their diet is well known. Hoffman's comments [1] are of interest in this connection:

Some of the tribes will adhere to the most disgusting varieties of food. . . . Some of the Shoshonees obtain some food from the settlements, but subsist chiefly upon what game and fish they can secure in addition to lizards, grasshoppers, etc. . . . Their mode of preparing grasshoppers is in this wise: A fire is built covering an area of from 20 to 30 feet square, and as the material is consumed to coals and ashes all the Indians start out and form an extensive circle, driving the grasshoppers with blankets or bunches of brush toward the center, where they are scorched or disabled, when they are collected, dried, and ground into meal. With the addition of a small quantity of water this is worked and kneaded into dough, formed into small cakes, and baked in the sand under a fire. . . . The Pah-Utes in the southwestern portion of Nevada, and even across the line into California, consume the larvæ of flies found upon the borders of some "alkali lakes." The organic matter washed ashore is soon covered with flies, where they deposit their eggs; there being not sufficient nourishment for all the worms, some die, when more eggs are deposited, and so on ad infinitum, until there is a belt of swarming, writhing worms from 2 to 4 feet broad and from an inch to 3 inches in depth. . . . At such localities the Indians congregate, scoop up and pack all that can be transported for present and future use. When thoroughly dried, it is ground into meal, and prepared and eaten as by the Shoshonees.

Where conditions of life are as hard as in many parts of the Southwest, it would be surprising indeed if, during times of special scarcity of food, all the Indians inhabiting the region have not been forced to rely on food which ordinarily they did not use; yet from the fact that Indians of various tribes have frequently been known to show a preference for raw entrails of large game animals and seem really fond of meat that has become somewhat tainted, one can not always feel certain that the use as food of things which are revolting to other people may not be due to choice.

The following Tewa names of kinds of insects were obtained:

Kuñæ refers to any kind of ant. Color- or size-denoting adjectives are often added. An anthill is called kuñæte·ḅi·ıì (k̑uñæ, ant; te·, house; ḅi·ıì, mound of small size; cf. ḅo·ıè, large mound). The Jemez, however, have two names for ant species: 'âmụ and wâ'âụm.

Hodge gives as Ant clans at various pueblos: Nambe, Kuⁿyï-tdóa; Pecos, Amú'+; Acoma, Sıí-hanoqᶜʰ; Sia, Sıí-háno; San Felipe, Sıí-háno.

Pæt'aḍa, bumblebee. These insects make honey. They are ground up and put into a dog's food in order to make him a good hunter, according to a San Ildefonso informant.

---

[1] Hoffman, W. J., Miscellaneous Ethnographic Observations on Indians Inhabiting Nevada, California, and Arizona, Tenth Ann. Rep. U. S. Geol. and Geog. Surv. Terr. for 1876 (Hayden Survey), pp. 465–66, 1878.

For species of wasp, bee, and hornet only two names could be obtained. *Qwoʻɹe̢be̢ʻ* seems to be the honey-bee, while *tʻawe* is some kind of wasp. Honey is called *qwoʻɹe̢be̢ʻʼą̊poʻ*, 'bee sweet water' (*qwoʻɹe̢be̢ʻ*, bee; *ʼą̊*, sweet, sweetness; *poʻ*, water).

Cushing tells how honey was obtained by Zuñi girls from a kind of burrowing hornet.[1]

In the Zuñi country there is a kind of burrowing hornet (or carpenter bee) which drills into adobe or mud walls and there deposits its honey. On any fine day in late summer one may see little groups of girls hunting the holes of these hornets along the garden walls. Whenever they find a number of them they provide themselves with gourds of water which they dash against the adobe or spurt into the holes through straws. The hornets, disabled by drenching, soon crawl forth and are easily killed or driven away, after which the girls, with little wooden or bone picks, dig out the honey.

Various species of butterfly are called at San Juan *poganini*, at San Ildefonso *polamimi*. The latter word is peculiar in that, so far as we know, it is the only native Tewa word which contains the sound of *l*. No word meaning "moth" could be obtained. The Isleta call butterfly *paiʃireɹe*.

The introduced house-fly and many insects of similar appearance are called *pʻųñų*. A bluish fly species was distinguished as *pʻųñų tsą̊ʻŋwæʻʼiʻi*, 'blue fly' (*pʻųñų*, fly; *tsą̊ʻŋwæʻ*, blue, green). Other Tanoan languages show cognate forms: Taos, *pʻuñuenâ;* Isleta, *pʻuñuɹe;* Piro (Bartlett's vocabulary), "*a-fu-ya-é,* fly"; Jemez, *ɹwijâ.*

Species of firefly are called *tsikʻowà* and *pʻaʻpʻųñų*, 'fire fly' (*pʻaʻ*, fire; *pʻųñų*, fly).

Dragon-flies are called *poʻdųŋdųŋ* (*poʻ*, water; *ɹųŋ*, to buzz like a bullroarer). Cushing tells a Zuñi myth of the origin of the dragon-fly.[2]

ʼɹųʻŋ, 'cricket,' 'locust.' This is the animal which the Mexicans call *chichara*.

Poʻtsiɹe, 'water bird' (*poʻ*, water; *tsiɹe*, bird), is not a bird, but an insect. It resembles *poʻdųŋdųŋ* in its habit of hovering over water.

Kʻowįʼiŋ is a species of grasshopper or locust. Another species is distinguished as *kʻowįʼiŋ ʼą̊ʻwiʼiʻ*, 'brown grasshopper' (*kʻowįʼiŋ*, grasshopper or locust species; *ʼą̊ʻ*, brown).

Black-headed head lice are called *pʻeʻ*. Body lice are known as *ʃuwà*, while bedbugs, which are still more numerous, are called *tʻįʼi*. All three terms might be carelessly applied to "lice" on plants, wood, or garbage. Notice that a small species of land snail is called *pʻųʻpʻeʻ*, 'rabbit-brush louse' (*pʻųʻ*, rabbit-brush; *pʻeʻ*, head louse); see page 65.

---

[1] Cushing, F. H., Zuñi Breadstuff, *The Millstone,* x, no. 3, March, 1885, p. 42, note.
[2] Ibid., pp. 35–38.

Mosquitoes are known as *fugo* or *fugo'e* (*fugo*, mosquito; *'e*, diminutive). Cf. Taos *qwitolaanâ;* Isleta *tankinaɹe;* Piro (Bartlett's vocabulary) "*quen-lo-a-tu-ya-é*"; Jemez *ṗáhárwijâ.*

The inch-long ill-smelling black beetle of the Tewa country is called *p'eǥapuˑsąɱe'e* (*p'eǥa*, to stink acridly; *puˑ*, base, buttocks, anus; *sąɲ*, ———— ?; *ḓe'e*, ————).

Poˑta·we (*po·*, squash, pumpkin; *ta·*, dry ?; *we*, ———— ?) are the same as *po·p'e·*, 'squash lice' (*po·*, squash, pumpkin; *p'e·*, head louse). The names refer to a kind of brown jumping bug seen on squash and pumpkin vines.

Worms of the most diverse kinds—maggots, larvæ, caterpillars, and almost any worm-like animals—are called *puƀæ·*. A hairy, fuzzy caterpillar is spoken of as *puƀæ· p'o'i'i*, 'hairy worm' (*puƀæ·*, worm; *p'o*, hairy, hair). The larvæ seen so plenteously at times on willow leaves are called *ja·ɲpuƀæ·*, 'willow worms' (*ja·ɲ*, willow; *puƀæ·*, worm). *Sa·puƀæ·*, 'manure worms' (*sa·*, manure; *puƀæ·*, worm) are the larvæ seen in manure; tape-worms, pin-worms, and other worms infesting the intestines are also called thus.

Angle-worms have a special name: *ną·ɲsi·* (*ną·ɲ*, earth; *si·*, unexplained).

CRUSTACEANS, MYRIAPODS, AND ARACHNIDS

Tse·ḱą·, 'spruce brownness' (*tse·*, Douglas spruce; *ḱą·*, buff-brown color, said to be so called because they are hairy like spruce trees, and brown) is applied to any kind of centipede, millipede, or myriapod. Many kinds are common. It is said that one bitten by a *tse·ḱą·* will live as many years as the animal has legs, which is usually a considerable number. The legs are called *k'o·*, 'arms,' as are also the legs of a spider.

Scorpions are very scarce. In the summer of 1911 Mr. K. A. Fleischer found one about half an inch long in the Rito de los Frijoles Canyon. The Tewa who have been asked do not know the name of this animal.

Any kind of spider is called *'ą'wæ·*. The second syllable of the word sounds just like *wæ·*, 'tooth,' and gives the name an ugly sound to Tewa ears. A spider web is called *'ą'wæ·p'e·*, 'spider trap' (*'ą'wæ·*, spider; *p'e·*, trap, snare). Tarantulas also are called *'ą'wæ·*, but the proper name is *ke·tu·pujè*, 'bear back deerskin' (*ke·*, bear, any species; *tu·*, back, spinal column; *pujè*, dressed skin of deer, elk, etc.). They are quite common. Their holes are called *p'o·*, 'hole.' An old Indian who is usually very correct in his identifications called a green dipterous insect taken from a *Populus angustifolia* tree *'ą'wæ· tsą·ɲwæ·'i'i*, 'blue or green spider' (*'ą'wæ·*, spider; *tsą·ɲwæ·*, blue, green).

MOLLUSKS [1]

The native Mollusca do not enter to any extent into the culture of
the Indians of this region at the present time, and probably the same
is true with reference to the former inhabitants.   It is not unusual
to find marine shells in the ruins, especially *Olivella*.   They were
probably obtained by barter with the peoples living to the southwestward.   At El Rito de los Frijoles a few specimens of *Olivella
biplicata* Sowerby and one of *Erato vitellina* Hinds were found.   They
doubtless were brought from southern California or from Lower California.   None of the native land or fresh-water shells of the region
have been found in the ruins, which is not surprising.   *Ashmunella,
Oreohelix, Physa*, and *Lymnæa* are the only species large enough to
be particularly noticed, and they do not exceed three-fourths of an
inch in greatest diameter.   This, it is true, is as large as the marine
shells commonly found in the ruins, but the land shells do not appear
to have become articles of barter, perhaps because they occur throughout the region and are therefore obtainable nearly everywhere and
further because they are rather fragile.

The shells of mollusks have been used as a medium of exchange
and as ornaments, amulets, and ceremonial objects by primitive
peoples everywhere.   They have been used very extensively by the
Indian tribes of the Pacific and Atlantic coastal regions in North
America and by them introduced into the interior.[2]   Strings of beads
made from the common *Olivella biplicata* of the Pacific coast, worn
about the neck as ornaments and used in barter, found their way into
Utah, Arizona, New Mexico, and southwestern Colorado, and Stearns[3]
tells us that in New Mexico Dr. Edward Palmer was "witness to a
trade wherein the consideration for a horse was a California abalone
shell."

Bracelets of *Glycimeris* from the Gulf of California have found their
way as far north and east at least as northeastern Arizona, where
they are reported, together with *Turritella tigrina, Conus*, and
Olivella, by Hough, who says[4] they are found mostly in the pueblo
ruins situated in mountain passes, probably along routes of primitive
travel.

[1] Henderson, Junius, Mollusca from Northern New Mexico, *The Nautilus*, XXVI, pp. 80–81, 1912.

[2] Holmes, William H., Art in Shell of the Ancient Americans, *Second Ann. Rep. Bur. Amer. Ethn., for
1880–81*, pp. 179–305, 1883; Report on the Ancient Ruins of Southwestern Colorado, Examined During the
Summers of 1875 and 1876, *Tenth Ann. Rep. U. S. Geol. and Geog. Sur. Terr. for 1876* (Hayden Survey), p.
407, 1878.   Stearns, Robert E. C., Ethno-Conchology—A Study of Primitive Money, *Ann. Rep. U. S.
Nat. Museum for 1887*, pp. 297–334, 1889.   Powers, Stephen, Tribes of California, *Contr. N. Amer. Ethn.*,
III, pp. 335–39, 1877.

[3] Stearns, R. E. C., op. cit., p. 329.

[4] Hough, Walter, Archæological Field Work in Northeastern Arizona: The Museum-Gates Expedition
of 1901, *Ann. Rep. U. S. Nat. Museum for 1901*, p. 295, 1903 (see also pp. 300, 305, 338, 344).

Fewkes [1] mentions West Coast marine shell ornaments in Arizona, made from *Pectunculus* [*Glycimeris*] sp., *Conus fergusoni*, *C. princeps*, *C. regularis*, *Turritella* sp., *Haliotis* sp., *Strombus* sp., *Cardium* sp., *Melongena patula*, *Oliva angulata*, and *Oliva* [*Olivella*] *biplicata* or *hiatula*, many of the species having also found their way into New Mexico. He says (p. 88):

It is well known that there was a considerable trade in early times in these shells, and long trips were taken by the Pueblo Indians for trade purposes.

The intercourse of northern and southern peoples of Arizona through trading expeditions continued to quite recent times, but judging from the number of specimens which were found in the ruins it must have been considerably greater in prehistoric times than it is at present. In fact, much of the decline in this traffic is probably to be traced to the modification of the southern Arizonian aborigines and the introduction of new ornaments by the whites.

From the ruins near Winslow, Arizona, the following species of Pacific coast marine shells have been reported by Fewkes: [2] *Pectunculus giganteus* Reeve, *Melongena patula* Rod. & Sow., *Strombus galeatus* Wood, *Conus fergusoni* Sow., *Cardium elatum* Sow., *Oliva angulata* Lam., *Oliva hiatula* Gmelin, *Oliva biplicata* Sow., *Turritella tigrina* Keiner.

Our San Ildefonso Indian informants had a distinct name for *Ashmunella*, which is common along El Rito de los Frijoles, in the Jemez Mountains, and probably in favorable localities throughout the region. They did not know *Oreohelix*, three specimens of which were obtained in the Jemez Mountains. *Pupilla*, although only 3 millimeters in height and 1.5 millimeter in width, received a special name, being distinguished from the more flatly spired shells by its high spire and cylindrical form. The flatter shells of small size (*Vallonia*, *Zonitoides*, etc.) were grouped under another name, without distinguishing species. One of the Indian boys, who had never noticed the snails before, was shown several species under some logs. He began a search and soon found a *Cochlicopa*, which differs markedly from the species that had been shown to him, and he at once recognized it as another kind of snail, but our informants had no distinct name for it.

The mollusks of the region have no apparent economic value. Conditions are not favorable in the Rio Grande Valley of northern New Mexico for the larger clams, which would have a food value, and none have been found.

There appear to be no published records of bivalve mollusks (*Pelecypoda*) for the region. *Calyculina* and *Pisidium* have been found in the Rio Grande drainage in Colorado, and the latter, if not the former, probably occurs in our area in New Mexico, wherever

[1] Fewkes, J.W., Two Summers' Work in Pueblo Ruins, *Twenty-second Ann. Rep. Bur. Amer. Ethn.*, part I, pp. 88–93, 187, 1904.
[2] Fewkes, J.W., Preliminary Account of an Expedition to the Pueblo Ruins Near Winslow, Arizona, in 1896, *Smithsonian Rep. for 1896*, pp. 529, 530, 535, 536, 1898.

there are perennial streams. Prof. T. D. A. Cockerell has a manuscript list of New Mexico shells prepared by Rev. E. H. Ashmun, in which *Pisidium* is listed from Santa Fe. In El Rito de los Frijoles no aquatic shells were found, either bivalve or univalve. Indeed, the scarcity of aquatic animal life, except water beetles and "water boatmen," may indicate that the water does not always flow in that rivulet in very dry seasons. The only record of an aquatic mollusk of any kind yet published is *Physa*, though *Lymnæa palustris* Müller from Taos, and *L. desidiosa* Say (probably *L. obrussa* Say) and *Planorbis parvus* Say, both from Santa Fe, are included in Ashmun's list.

Land snails are usually to be found along the bottom lands, in the canyons, and throughout the mountains, under cottonwood and aspen logs, not often among conifers. As the species are mostly tiny, some of them smaller than an ordinary pin head, and most of them much less than a quarter of an inch in diameter, it requires close inspection to discover them. They may be packed with a little moss or some green leaves and shipped alive to conchologists for identification.

? ———

Ashmunella thomsoniana Ancey.

This species is recorded from Santa Fe Canyon and the Pecos Valley by Pilsbry,[1] the localities being all east of the Rio Grande. Two subspecies are credited to the Pecos drainage in New Mexico. Other species are recorded from south of our area.

P'e'oᵬe'e·, 'little wood shell' (p'e, stick, wood; 'oᵬe, shell; 'e·, diminutive).

Ashmunella ashmuni Dall.

The type locality of this species is Bland, not far from El Rito de los Frijoles.[2] The species is very abundant at several localities along the Rito de los Frijoles. Five immature specimens from near the top of the Jemez Mountains at Valle Grande, and four from about halfway to the base of the mountains, may be referable to this form, though probably belonging to the next. It is likely that the San Ildefonso Indian name given to this form would be applied to the other *Ashmunella* species, as they are so much alike that they would be separated only by a skilled conchologist looking for slight differences.

? ———

Ashmunella ashmuni robusta Pilsbry.

This subspecies is somewhat larger than the preceding, and was described as from the "Jemez Mountains near Bland, N. Mex., at higher elevations than *A. ashmuni*."[3]

[1] Pilsbry, Henry A., Mollusca of the Southwestern States, I: Urocoptidæ; Helicidæ of Arizona and New Mexico, *Proc. Acad. Nat. Sci. Phila.*, LVII, p. 235, 1905.
[2] Dall, William H., Report on the Mollusks Collected by the International Boundary Commission of the United States and Mexico, *Proc. U. S. Nat. Museum*, XIX, p. 342, 1897. Pilsbry, Henry A., op. cit., p. 233.
[3] Pilsbry, Henry A., op. cit., p. 233.

Ashmunella townsendi Bartsch.

Described from Ruidoso, Lincoln County, New Mexico.[1]

? ———

Oreohelix strigosa depressa Ckll.

Three weathered specimens which appear to belong to some form of *O. strigosa* Gould were found in the Jemez Mountains near Valle Grande. Our Indian informants were not familiar with them and had no name for them, but did not confuse them with *Ashmunella*. Ashmun's list, hereinbefore mentioned, includes *Oreohelix concentrata* Dall, from near Bland, at an altitude of 10,000 feet.

? ———

Pupilla muscorum Linné.

We found a single specimen at El Rito de los Frijoles.

? ———

Pupilla blandi Morse.

Abundant at El Rito de los Frijoles and in the Jemez Mountains near Valle Grande.

? ———

Bifidaria pellucida parvidens Sterki.

We found one in a canyon half-way to the top of Jemez Mountains, near Valle Grande.

? ———

Vertigo coloradensis basidens Pilsbry & Vanatta.

The type locality is Bland, New Mexico.[2]

? ———

Vertigo concinnula Cockerell.

We found two specimens of this species in the Jemez Mountains, near Valle Grande. It was recorded from these mountains by Pilsbry and Vanatta also.[3]

? ———

Cochlicopa lubrica Müller.

Common at El Rito de los Frijoles.

? ———

Vallonia cyclophorella Ancey.

Common in the Jemez Mountains, near Valle Grande, and abundant in the canyon at El Rito de los Frijoles.

---

[1] Bartsch in *Smithson. Misc. Coll.*, XLVII, pp. 13–14, 1904.

[2] Pilsbry, Henry A., and Vanatta, Edward G., A Partial Revision of the Pupæ of the United States, *Proc. Acad. Nat. Sci. Phila. for 1900*, p. 604.

[3] Pilsbry, Henry A., and Vanatta, Edward G., op. cit., pp. 599–600.

? ————

Vitrina alaskana Dall.

We found three small dead specimens in the Jemez Mountains, near Valle Grande, and four at El Rito de los Frijoles.

? ————

Euconulus trochiformis alaskensis Pilsbry.

Common at El Rito de los Frijoles, and one specimen found in the Jemez Mountains near Valle Grande.

? ————

Zonitoides arboreus Say.

Common in the Jemez Mountains, near Valle Grande, and abundant at El Rito de los Frijoles.

? ————

Pyramidula shimeki cockerelli Pilsbry.

At El Rito de los Frijoles only two specimens were found at the ancient pueblo, while about two miles up the canyon from the pueblo the species was abundantly represented.

? ————

Succinea avara Say.

Only one specimen found at El Rito de los Frijoles. We dare suspect that Yarrow's record of *S. stretchiana* Bland at Tierra Amarilla [1] may refer to this species.

? ————

Physa sp.

Yarrow [2] recorded *P. ancillaria* Say from San Ildefonso, *P. traskii* Lea from Santa Fe, *?P. D'Orbigniana* Lea and *P. warreniana* Lea from Abiquiu, and *P. altonensis* from Pescado. It is likely that these identifications are partly or wholly wrong, but evidently one or more species of *Physa* occur in the region.

Yarrow's record of *Pyramidula perspectiva* Say at San Ildefonso [3] is probably something else, possibly *P. cronkhitei anthonyi*.

P'ɯ·p'e·, 'rabbit-brush louse' (*p'ɯ*, rabbit-brush; *p'e·*, head louse).
Pupilla sp.

The species were consistently called thus whether found on rabbit-brush bushes or elsewhere. (See p. 59.)

We have attempted to record all the Tewa names for species of Mollusca or their shells, and with this intent we have spent considerable time examining collections of shells with a number of Indians.

---

[1] Yarrow, H. C., Report upon the Collections of Terrestrial and Fluviatile Mollusca Made in Portions of Colorado, Utah, New Mexico, and Arizona During the Years 1872, 1873, and 1874, *U. S. Geog. Explor. & Surv. W. of 100th Merid.* (Wheeler Survey), v, p. 936, 1875.

[2] Ibid., pp. 939, 940, 941.

[3] Ibid., p. 932.

The Tewa were familar with mollusks living in their own country, and also with shells of mollusks obtained from other tribes and used for ceremonial or other purposes.

The general name for fresh-water snails is 'oƀe, a word applied also to some kinds of marine mollusks and their shells. (See below.)

Slugs are called puƀæ·, a name which is applied to any wormlike animal. (See under the discussion of insects, page 60.)

Only the shells of marine mollusks are known, although our inform-ants had quite a correct idea of what the living animals are like.

The following terms referring to shells were recorded: 'oƀe p̂i·'i'i, 'red shell' ('oƀe, shell; p̂i·, red); 'oƀe t'igiᶇḍi'i, 'flat shell' ('oƀe, shell; t'igiᶇ, flat and roundish); 'oƀe mapi'i'i, 'spiral shell' ('oƀe, shell; mapi, spiral, twisted); 'oƀe k̂a·'i'i, 'thick shell' ('oƀe, shell; k̂a·, thick); 'oƀe k̂o·'i'i, 'rough shell' ('oƀe, shell; k̂o·, rough); 'oƀe p̂a·'i'i, 'rough shell with surface cracked' ('oƀe, shell; p̂a·, cracked, chapped); 'oƀe ᶇwæ·'i'i, 'spiny shell' ('oƀe, shell; ᶇwæ·, spiny, spine; spiky, spike, thorny, thorn). To pectens the term 'oƀe hegè wigèwigè'i'i, 'shell wavy with little grooves' ('oƀe, shell; hegè, arroyito, rivulet, groove; wigèwigè, wavy, undulating, sinuous) is applied. To pectens and also to other bivalves with undulating edge the term 'oƀe puᶇwæ sæ·ᶇwi'i'i, 'beautiful zigzagged shell' ('oƀe, shell; puᶇwæ, beautiful to look at; sæ·ᶇwi, zigzagged, zigzag) is applied.

The abalone shell is called 'eɉi. This is the kind of shell which the Salt Old Woman used as a handkerchief, according to a Santa Clara myth obtained by Miss B. W. Freire-Marreco. The 'eɉi which she had was soft as a handkerchief. A large abalone shell is sometimes called 'eɉisæ'æwè, 'abalone vessel' ('eɉi, abalone; sæ'æwè, bowl-shaped vessel). Abalone shells are frequently referred to with accompanying color-denoting adjectives. Thus 'eɉi t̂sæ·'i'i, 'white abalone shell' ('eɉi, abalone shell; t̂sæ·, white); 'eɉi tsǫ́·ᶇwæ·'i'i, 'blue or green abalone shell' ('eɉi, abalone shell; tsǫ́·ᶇwæ·, blue, green); 'eɉi t̂se·tǫ́'aᶇḍi'i, 'yellow painted abalone shell' ('eɉi, abalone shell; t̂se·, yellow; tǫ́'aᶇ, painted).

A mussel shell and a razor clam shell were also called 'eɉi, how correctly we are not certain. Beads made of abalone shell are called 'eɉikwa'a, 'abalone beads' ('eɉi, abalone; kwa'a, bead).

Cowrie shells, coffee shells, and the like, are called 'oga. Descriptive adjectives are often added. The term 'oga is also applied to olivella shells, whelk shells, and the like.

There is some kind of spiral univalve which is called tinini. Inspec-tion of large collections of shells with the informants failed to reveal what kind of shell this may be. The tinini are described as being about an inch long. They are worn by the Kosa or Chifonetes on

certain occasions. Miss B. W. Freire-Marreco has seen them, but
has not identified them.

A kind of large, thick, flat shell, evidently a bivalve, is called
tsαлαmʉ. Not even all of the older people at San Ildefonso know
this shell or its name. Our informants were not sure with regard to
its color.

A kind of white, flat shell about 6 inches across is called *ʦǽˑtˀaˑ*,
'white flat' (*ʦǽˑ*, white; *tˀaˑ*, flat and roundish). The *ʦǽˑtˀaˑ* was
sometimes worn on the breast of Tewa men. It was also cut up and
made into beads.

A kind of large spiral univalve from which beads were formerly
made is called *p̂oˑtsunʉ.*

A sort of shell described as white, cylindrical, 2 inches or more
long and about a quarter of an inch in diameter, is called *ʦǽˑwijè.*
These shells, which were highly valued, were strung and worn as
necklaces. Now only bone imitations of these shells are to be found
at the Tewa pueblos, but these are also called *ʦǽˑwijè.* The name
ʦǽˑwijè sounds like 'white two' (*ʦǽˑ*, white; *wijè*, two), but this
makes no sense.

Hodge gives *Kwátsei-tdóa* as a Shell Bead clan of San Ildefonso.
Kwa'a ʦǽˑʼiʼi îowà means 'white bead clan' (*kwa'a*, bead made of
any substance, not necessarily shell; *ʦǽˑ*, white; *îowà*, person,
people).

THE LOWER INVERTEBRATES

Very little is known of the lower forms of invertebrate life of
northern New Mexico, and from an ethnological point of view such
forms are mostly unimportant. While some of the pathological Pro-
tozoa must have had an important bearing on the health of the ancient
peoples of this region, just as they affect the present population, as
active agents in the spread of disease, yet such minute objects could
not have been known to people who had no microscopes. It is not
likely that any of the other phyla below the Mollusca are well represented here, if they occur at all, except the worms and their allies,
and very little work appears to have been done with respect to them.
Verrill [1] reported two unnamed varieties of leech, one at Taos and
one at San Ildefonso. We collected no specimens and so obtained
neither Indian names for nor Indian lore concerning them.

---

[1] Verrill, A. E., Report upon the Collections of Fresh Water Leeches Made in Portions of Nevada, Utah,
Colorado, New Mexico, and Arizona During the Years 1872, 1873, and 1874, *U. S. Geog. Explor. & Surv.
W. of 100th Merid., Final Report,* v, p. 965, 1875.

CORAL

$\widehat{Ku} \cdot \hat{pi}\cdot$, 'red stone' ($ku\cdot$, stone; $\hat{pi}\cdot$, red).

Red coral.

Red coral beads were obtained by the Tewa from tribes living in the south. The beads were usually already made and strung when the Tewa obtained them. The beads were called either $ku \cdot \hat{pi}$ simply, or $ku \cdot \hat{pi} \cdot kwa'a$, 'red coral beads' ($ku\cdot$, stone; $\hat{pi}\cdot$, red; $kwa'a$, bead). No other kind or color of coral seems to have been known to the Tewa.

As Coral clans of various pueblos Hodge gives: San Juan, $Kopi^n$-$td\acute{o}a;$ Santa Clara, $Kupi$-$t\acute{o}da;$ San Ildefonso, $Kupi^n$-$td\acute{o}a;$ Tesuque, $Kupi^n$-$td\acute{o}a;$ San Felipe, $Y\acute{a}scha$-$h\acute{a}no$ (coral bead). Hodge, quoting Fewkes, also gives $K\acute{o}peli$-$t\acute{o}wa$ as a Pink Conch Shell clan of Hano. The Rio Grande Tewa know no such shell. (Can it be for $\widehat{Ku} \cdot \hat{pi}\cdot$?)

BIBLIOGRAPHY

ALLEN, HARRISON. A monograph of the bats of North America. *Bull. 43, U. S. Nat. Museum*, 1893.

ALLEN, J. A. Revision of the Chickarees, or North American red squirrels (subgenus *Tamiasciurus*). *Bull. Amer. Mus. Nat. Hist.*, X, pp. 247–298, 1898.

—— History of the American bison, Bison americanus. *Ninth Ann. Rep. U. S. Geol. and Geog. Surv. Terr.* (Hayden Survey) *for 1875*, pp. 443–587, 1877.

—— *See also* COUES, ELLIOTT, *and* ALLEN.

AMERICAN ORNITHOLOGISTS' UNION, Committee on Nomenclature. Check-list of North American birds. New York, 1910.

BAILEY, FLORENCE MERRIAM. Handbook of birds of the western United States. Boston, 1902.

—— Additional notes on the birds of the upper Pecos. *The Auk*, XXI, pp. 349–363, 1904.

—— Additions to Mitchell's list of the summer birds of San Miguel county, New Mexico. Ibid., pp. 443–449, 1904.

—— Notes from northern New Mexico. Ibid., XXII, pp. 316–318, 1905.

BAILEY, VERNON. Revision of American voles of the genus Microtus. *North American Fauna, no. 17, Biol. Surv., U. S. Dept. Agr.*, 1900.

—— Wolves in relation to stock, game, and the National Forest reserves. *Bull. no. 72, Forest Service, U. S. Dept. Agr.*, 1907.

—— Destruction of wolves and coyotes. *Circ. no. 63, Biol. Surv., U. S. Dept. Agr.*, 1908.

BANDELIER, A. F. Final report of investigations among the Indians of the southwestern United States, carried on mainly in the years from 1880 to 1885. Part II. *Papers Archæol. Inst. Amer., Amer. Ser.*, IV, 1892.

—— The delight makers. New York, 1890.

BARTSCH, PAUL. A new Ashmunella from New Mexico. *Smithson. Misc. Coll.*, XLVII, pp. 13–14, 1904.

BRINTON, DANIEL G. The American race. New York, 1891.

BROWN, ARTHUR ERWIN. A review of the genera and species of American snakes north of Mexico. *Proc. Acad. Nat. Sci. Phila.*, LIII, pp. 10–110, 1901.

COCKERELL, T. D. A. The fishes of the Rocky Mountain region. *Univ. Colo. Studies*, V, pp. 159–178, 1908.

—— The nomenclature of the American fishes usually called Leuciscus and Rutilus. *Proc. Biol. Soc. Wash.*, XXII, pp. 215–217, 1909.

COPE, EDWARD D. Report on the geology of that part of northwestern New Mexico examined during the field season of 1874. *Ann. Rep. U. S. Geog. Explor. & Surv. W. of 100th Merid. for 1875* (Wheeler Survey), pp. 61–97, 1875.

—— Report upon the extinct vertebrata obtained in New Mexico by parties of the expedition of 1874. Ibid., *Final Report*, IV, pt. II, 1877.

—— The batrachia of North America. *Bull. 34, U. S. Nat. Museum*, 1889.

—— The crocodilians, lizards, and snakes of North America. *Ann. Rep. U. S. Nat. Museum for 1898*, pp. 153–1270, 1900.

—— *and* YARROW, H. C. Report upon the collections of fishes made in portions of Nevada, Utah, California, Colorado, New Mexico, and Arizona, during the years 1871, 1872, 1873, and 1874. *Final Rep. U. S. Geog. Expl. and Surv. W. of 100th Merid.* (Wheeler Survey), V, pp. 635–705, 1875.

COUES, ELLIOTT. The prairie wolf, or coyoté: Canis latrans. *Amer. Nat.*, VII, pp. 385–389, 1873.

Coues, Elliott, *and* Allen, Joel Asaph. Monographs of North American Rodentia. *Final Rep. U. S. Geol. Surv. Terr.* (Hayden Survey), xi, 1877.

Coues, Elliott, *and* Yarrow, H. C. Report upon the collections of mammals made in portions of Nevada, Utah, California, Colorado, New Mexico, and Arizona, during the years 1871, 1872, 1873, and 1874. *Final Report U. S. Geog. Expl. and Surv. W. of 100th Merid.* (Wheeler Survey), v, pp. 35–129, 1875.

Cushing, F. H. Zuñi breadstuff. *The Millstone*, ix, no. 3, March, 1884; x, no. 3, March, 1885; x, no. 4, April, 1885.

Dall, William H. Report on the mollusks collected by the International Boundary Commission of the United States and Mexico, 1892–1894. *Proc. U. S. Nat. Museum*, xix, pp. 333–379, 1897.

Dickerson, Mary C. The frog book. New York, 1906.

Ditmars, Raymond Lee. The reptile book. New York, 1907.

Dorsey, George A., *and* Kroeber, Alfred L. Traditions of the Arapaho. *Pub. Field Columb. Mus., Anthr. ser.*, v, 1903.

Evermann, Barton W. *See* Jordan, David Starr, *and* Evermann.

Ferriss, J. H. *See* Pilsbry, H. A., *and* Ferriss.

Fewkes, J. Walter. Pacific coast shells from prehistoric Tusayan pueblos. *Amer. Anthr.*, ix, pp. 359–367, 1896.

——— Preliminary account of an expedition to the pueblo ruins near Winslow, Arizona, in 1896. *Ann. Rep. Smithsonian Institution for 1896*, pp. 517–539, 1898.

——— Property-right in eagles among the Hopi. *Amer. Anthr.*, n. s., ii, 690 et seq., 1900.

——— Two summers' work in pueblo ruins. *Twenty-second Rep. Bur. Amer. Ethn.*, pp. 3–195, 1904.

Fisher, A. K. A partial list of Moki animal names. *Amer. Anthr.*, ix, p. 174, 1896.

Fletcher, Alice C. The Hako, a Pawnee ceremony. *Twenty-second Rep. Bur. Amer. Ethn.*, pt. 2, pp. 5–368, 1904.

Gatschet, A. S. Zwölf Sprachen aus dem Südwesten Nordamerikas. Weimar, 1876,

Gilman, M. French. Birds on the Navajo reservation in New Mexico. *The Condor*, x, pp. 146–152, 1908.

Goldman, Edward A. Revision of the wood rats of the genus Neotoma. *North American Fauna, no. 31, Biol. Surv.*, U. S. Dept. Agr., 1910.

Goss, Nathaniel S. The white-necked raven (Corvus cryptoleucus) in New Mexico. *Bull. Nutt. Orn. Club.*, vi, p. 118, 1881.

Guinn, J. M. Historical and biographical record of southern California. Chicago, 1902.

Henderson, Junius. The mollusca of Colorado. *Univ. Colo. Studies*, iv, pts. 1, 2, pp. 77–96, 167–185, 1907.

——— Mollusca from northern New Mexico. *The Nautilus*, xxvi, pp. 80–81, 1912.

Henry, T. Charlton. Notes derived from observations made on the birds of New Mexico during the years 1853 and 1854. *Proc. Acad. Nat. Sci. Phila.*, vii, pp. 306–317, 1856.

——— Catalogue of the birds of New Mexico as compiled from notes and observations made while in that territory, during a residence of six years. Ibid., xi, pp. 104–109, 1860.

Henshaw, H. W. Report upon the ornithological collections made in portions of Nevada, Utah, California, Colorado, New Mexico, and Arizona during the years 1871, 1872, 1873, and 1874. *U. S. Geog. Expl. & Surv. W. of 100th Merid.* (Wheeler Survey), v, pp. 131–507, 1875.

——— Note on Lagopus leucurus and Leucosticte australis. *The Auk*, xxii, pp. 315–316, 1905.

——— *and* Nelson, E. W. List of birds observed in summer and fall on the upper Pecos river, New Mexico. Ibid., ii, pp. 326–333, 1885; iii, pp. 73–80, 1886.

HERRICK, C. L., TERRY, JOHN, and HERRICK, N. H. Notes on a collection of lizards from New Mexico. *Bull. 1, Univ. New Mex.*, pp. 117–148, 1899. (Repr. from *Bull. Sci. Lab. Denison Univ.*, XI.)

HODGE, F. W. Pueblo Indian clans. *Amer. Anthr.*, IX, pp. 345–352, 1896.

HOFFMAN, W. J. Miscellanous ethnographic observations on Indians inhabiting Nevada, California, and Arizona. *Tenth Ann. Rep. U. S. Geol. and Geog. Surv. Terr. for 1876* (Hayden Survey), pp. 461–478, 1878.

———— The Menomini Indians. *Fourteenth Rep. Bur. Amer. Ethn.*, pp. 3–328, 1896.

HOLLISTER, N. A systematic synopsis of the muskrats. *North American Fauna, no. 17, Biol. Surv.*, U. S. Dept. Agr., 1911.

HOLMES, WM. H. Report on the ancient ruins of southwestern Colorado, examined during the summers of 1875 and 1876. *Tenth Ann. Rep. U. S. Geol. and Geog. Surv. Terr. for 1876* (Hayden Survey), pp. 383–408, 1878.

———— Art in shell of the ancient Americans. *Second Rep. Bur. Amer. Ethn.*, pp. 179–305, 1883.

HORNADAY, WILLIAM T. The extermination of the American bison. *Ann. Rep. U. S. Nat. Museum for 1887*, pp. 367–548, 1889.

HOUGH, WALTER. Archeological field work in northeastern Arizona (The Museum-Gates Expedition of 1901). *Ann. Rep. U. S. Nat. Mus. for 1901*, pp. 287–358, 1903.

———— Pueblo environment. *Proc. Amer. Asso. Adv. Sci.*, LV, pp. 447–454, 1906.

JORDAN, DAVID STARR, and EVERMANN, BARTON W. The fishes of North and Middle America. *Bull. 47, U. S. Nat. Mus.*, 1896–1900. 4 vols.

KENNERLY, C. B. R. Report on the birds collected on route. *Zoological Rep. no. 3, U. S. Explor. & Surv. for R. R. from Miss. to Pac. Ocean* (Whipple Survey), X, 1859.

LANGKAVEL, B. Dogs and savages. *Smithsonian Rep. for 1898*, pp. 651–675, 1899. (Transl. from *Intern. Archiv fur Ethnog.*, Bd. VIII, pp. 109–149.)

LUCAS, F. A. A dog of the ancient Pueblos. *Science*, n. s., V, p. 544, 1897.

LYON, M. W. JR. Mammal remains from two prehistoric village sites in New Mexico and Arizona. *Proc. U. S. Nat. Mus.*, XXXI, pp. 647–649, 1906.

MCCALL, GEORGE A. Some remarks on the habits, etc., of birds met with in western Texas, between San Antonio and the Rio Grande, and in New Mexico. *Proc. Acad. Nat. Sci. Phila. for 1851*, V, pp. 213–224, 1852.

———— Notes on Carpodacus frontalis, (Say) with description of a new species of the same genus from Santa Fe, New Mexico. Ibid., VI, p. 61, 1854.

MCGEE, W J. The Siouan Indians. *Fifteenth Rep. Bur. Amer. Ethn.*, pp. 153–204, 1897.

MEARNS, EDGAR A. Mammals of the Mexican boundary of the United States. *Bull. 56, U. S. Nat. Museum*, pt. 1, 1907.

———— Ornithological vocabulary of the Moki Indians. *Amer. Anthr.*, IX, pp. 391–403, 1896.

MERRIAM, C. HART. Descriptions of twenty-three new pocket gophers of the genus Thomomys. *Proc. Biol. Soc. Wash.*, XIV, pp. 107–117, 1901.

MILLER, GERRIT S. Revision of the North American bats of the family Vespertilionidæ. *North American Fauna, no. 13, Biol. Surv.*, U. S., Dept. Agr., 1897.

———— A new jumping mouse from New Mexico. *Proc. Biol. Soc. Wash.*, XXIV, pp. 253–254, 1911.

MITCHELL, WALTON I. The summer birds of San Miguel county, New Mexico. *The Auk*, XV, pp. 306–311, 1898.

MOONEY, JAMES. Myths of the Cherokee. *Nineteenth Rep. Bur. Amer. Ethn.*, pp. 3–548, 1900.

MORRISON, CHARLES C. Executive and descriptive report of Lieutenant Charles C. Morrison, Sixth Cavalry, on the operations of party no. 2, Colorado section, field season of 1877. *Ann. Rep. U. S. Geog. Expl. and Surv. W. 100th Merid., for 1878*, pp. 131–139, 1878.

NADAILLAC, *Marquis de*. Pre-historic America. New York, 1884.

NELSON, E. W. The rabbits of North America. *North American Fauna, no. 29, Biol. Surv., U. S. Dept. Agr.*, 1909.

—— *See* HENSHAW, H. W., *and* NELSON.

OSGOOD, WILFRED H. Revision of the pocket mice of the genus Perognathus. Ibid., no. 18, 1900.

—— Revision of the mice of the American genus Peromyscus. Ibid., no. 28, 1909.

PILSBRY, HENRY A. Mollusca of the Southwestern states. I: Urocoptidæ; Helicidæ of Arizona and New Mexico. *Proc. Acad. Nat. Sci. Phila.*, LVII, pp. 211–290, 1905; LXI, pp. 495–516, 1909; LXII, pp. 44–147, 1910.

—— *and* FERRISS, J. H. Mollusca of the Southwestern states. II. Ibid., LVIII, pp. 123–175, 1906.

—— *and* VANATTA, EDWARD G. A partial revision of the Pupæ of the United States. Ibid., 1900, pp. 582–611, 1901.

PREBLE, EDWARD A. Revision of the jumping mice of the genus Zapus. *North American Fauna, no. 15, Biol. Surv., U. S. Dept. Agr.*, 1899.

RUSSELL, FRANK. The Pima Indians. *Twenty-sixth Ann. Rep. Bur. Amer. Ethn.*, pp. 3–389, 1908.

RUTHVEN, ALEXANDER G. A collection of reptiles and amphibians from southern New Mexico and Arizona. *Bull. Amer. Mus. Nat. Hist.*, XXIII, pp. 483–603, 1907.

—— Variations and genetic relationships of the garter-snakes. *Bull. 61, U. S. Nat. Museum*, 1908.

SPRINGER, FRANK. The field session of the School of American Archæology. *Science*, n. s., XXXII, 623, 1910.

STEARNS, ROBERT E. C. Ethno-conchology: a study of primitive money. *Ann. Rep. U. S. Nat. Museum for 1887*, pp. 297–334, 1889.

STEJNEGER, LEONHARD. The poisonous snakes of North America. Ibid., 1893, pp. 345–487, 1895.

—— Annotated list of reptiles and batrachians collected by Dr. C. Hart Merriam and Vernon Bailey on the San Francisco mountain plateau and desert of the Little Colorado, Arizona, with descriptions of new species. *North American Fauna, no. 3, Biol. Surv., U. S. Dept. Agr.*, pp. 103–118, 1890.

STEVENSON, MATILDA COXE. The Zuñi Indians. *Twenty-third Rep. Bur. Amer. Ethn.*, pp. 1–608, 1904.

VANATTA, EDWARD G. *See* PILSBRY, H. A., *and* VANATTA.

VERRILL, A. E. Report upon the collections of fresh water leeches made in portions of Nevada, Utah, Colorado, New Mexico, and Arizona during the years 1872, 1873, and 1874. *U. S. Geog. Explor. & Surv. W. of 100th Merid.* (Wheeler Survey), V, pp. 955–967, 1875.

VOTH, H. R. Hopi proper names. *Pub. Field Columb. Mus., Anthr. ser.*, VI, pp. 63–113, 1905.

WARREN, EDWARD ROYAL. The mammals of Colorado. New York, 1910.

WINSHIP, GEORGE PARKER. The Coronado expedition, 1540–1542. *Fourteenth Rep. Bur. Amer. Ethn.*, pp. 329–613, 1896.

YARROW, H. C. Report upon the collections of batrachians and reptiles made in portions of Nevada, Utah, California, Colorado, New Mexico, and Arizona, during the years 1871, 1872, 1873, and 1874. *U. S. Geog. Explor. & Surv. W. of 100th Merid.* (Wheeler Survey), V, pp. 509–633, 1875.

—— Report upon the collections of terrestrial and fluviatile mollusca made in portions of Colorado, Utah, New Mexico, and Arizona during the years 1872, 1873, and 1874. Ibid., pp. 923–954.

—— Check-list of North American reptilia and batrachia, with catalogue of specimens in U. S. National Museum. *Bull. 24, U. S. Nat. Museum*, 1882.

INDEX OF ZOOLOGICAL NAMES

74

O